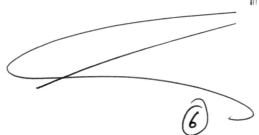

The Bounce Back Journey of Men's Health

AN INSPIRING COLLECTION OF PERSONAL STORIES

Compiled by
Discover Your Bounce Publishing

DEDICATION

To Jacob. You inspired us and started a movement.

CONTENTS

FOREWORD
By TV Presenter Martin Roberts

Which cruel twist of evolutionary fate resulted in us blokes being the way we are?

Did cave men throw themselves from rocky outcrops if the brontosaurus haul wasn't up to scratch?

Did our mediaeval male ancestors not bother to worry those around them when bits of them were acting unusually or falling off?

Whatever happened, we've ended up with 50% of the population, by and large, being really rubbish at looking after itself.

Oh, sure, when things are going normally we get by quite well. The moment life throws us a curveball, our primaeval adrenaline and survival instincts may get us through the immediate danger or issues. But once that imminent threat has gone, we are utterly crap at repairing the physical and mental wounds that may have been inflicted.

It's why so many preventable diseases go undiagnosed before it's too late. My best mate died of bowel cancer at 54, and I swear it's down to a combination of struggling on without help in extremely difficult personal circumstances, and not visiting the doctor sooner when things weren't right when he went to the loo.

This book contains some truly inspiring stories of survival against the odds in situations that could not be avoided. But for sure there is so much more we can do to prevent incurable problems occurring. And looking after your mind and taking its health seriously is a massively important step on the road to overall wellness.

The stigma attached to mental health has slowly been eroded over recent years, with high profile figures- especially men- revealing for the first time the inner turmoil behind their confident exteriors.

Like ducks in a fast flowing stream it seems it's a common trait that we manage to retain composure, when underneath we are paddling like there's no tomorrow.

And sadly for some the effort becomes so great that there literally is no tomorrow, as suicide claims its alarmingly high number of victims.

So there is still a long way to go until it's second nature for us to acknowledge our struggles and reach out for support before it's too late. But a large step in the right direction is recognising that others feel the same. Currently. Previously. In the future. And that no matter how 'crazy' or extreme the feelings are, many, many people will have shared them.

Which is why the collection of personal experiences told in this book are so invaluable. Hopefully by reading about others' struggles and their reaction to them, you will be touched inspired and relieved. Relieved that you are not alone. You will see that perhaps, like you, many people procrastinate and allow issues, physical and mental, to multiply exponentially before dealing with them.

And I've been there. I've let life's challenges get to a point where they seem so overwhelming that I've stood on an underground station platform and considered taking a step forward just before the next train arrives. Perhaps it was only the annoyed, *"Will you PLEASE stop pacing!"* from a fellow commuter that snapped me from my potentially catastrophically negative state. Perhaps I would have realised the inadequacies and insanity of that solution at the last minute. But once the fog of depression had cleared, I promised myself I would never allow myself to get to such a perilous position ever again. But I can certainly empathise with the feeling that it really is, "All too much".

So, I hope you enjoy our stories of self discovery, and that you promise you will reach out for help if you need it, and never find yourself on that lonely underground platform.

ANDREW HOOK

Andy is a dad of two (Grace, 13 and James, 11) and husband to Sarah for 18 years; he enjoys rugby, cycling and camping with the family, in no particular order!

Last year, aged 49, Andy was diagnosed with neck/throat cancer. He accepted the diagnosis, and used a Stoical mindset to focus on dealing with cancer in a positive manner.

Andy has an automotive background of over thirty years, and uses this to great effect to help clients in his capacity as the founder of ARH Vehicle Solutions – a Bristol-based leasing brokerage who provide impartial, and sometimes blunt, advice to individuals and businesses in the southwest (and further afield). Andy's humour and light-hearted manner has helped him to be fondly received in the Bristol business community.

Whether he is in the business, rugby or another community Andy loves engaging with and helping wherever possible.

This possibly is why his company motto is - 'Always Ready to Help!'

Follow these links to connect with Andy:

https://arhvehiclesolutions.co.uk/

https://www.facebook.com/leasingkeptsimple

https://twitter.com/veh1clesolution

Or send him an e-mail: andy@arhvehiclesolutions.co.uk

Get Yourself Checked – Even if it is a Pain in the Neck!

I am one of those people who rarely visits their doctor.

So, when I noticed a lump on my throat I was a bit concerned, as it didn't seem to be soft like a swollen gland. I booked to see my GP to get it checked out. She put my mind at ease, as she didn't think it was anything to worry about, but booked me in for an ultrasound just to check.

Later that week, I went to the ultrasound appointment to satisfy my GP. The radiographer felt around my throat with the scanner and made comments to say that he didn't think there was anything to worry about. He asked if it was okay to take some fluid samples to send off to check, which I didn't mind (other than the needle bloody well hurting!).

I left the hospital relativity confident that there was nothing to worry about, but it was better to be safe than sorry.

I was then busy getting the car packed and ready to go on our annual camping trip to Dorset, so didn't really have the time to think about the results etc. We were happily enjoying the great weather and the beach at Weymouth when my wife suggested we go to Kingston Lacy the next day. We loaded the car up with my family (wife, kids and grandparents) and made our way down to Kingston Lacy.

On the way there I missed a call from an unknown number, but did not pay much attention to it. When we got into the car park I thought that I spotted our former neighbour's car, but thought it was highly unlikely as they now lived in East Sussex.

Amazingly it was our neighbours, so we all sat down in the café to catch-up and have a chat. I felt my mobile buzz again with a missed call. I was on holiday so didn't really want to be checking my phone all the time, but this same unknown number had called again! This time they had left a voicemail message, so I listened to the message.

"Mr Hook - this is Clevedon Cottage Hospital calling regarding your results from the ultrasound blood/fluid samples. If you could call us back at your earliest opportunity, we would really appreciate it."

All of a sudden it dawned on me that maybe things were not okay after all!

The downside of going to a country house in Dorset is the shocking mobile coverage! I paced up and down in the grounds trying to find somewhere with some signal in order for me to call the hospital back. Eventually, I managed to get through, but ended up leaving a voicemail message for the doctor to call me back. This went on for a while as the doctor then left a message for me etc, etc! I explained to my wife what I was doing and that it wasn't me taking work calls on holiday!

I then went back to the one spot where there was a signal and tried a few times again, but it kept going to the answerphone. I decided to stay there for a while just in case the doctor rang back.

It dawned on me that this could be something serious! My internal thoughts started to think of what it could possibly be. It was at this moment that I decided that I would allow myself to be quite calm whilst thinking through what could be happening. I had started reading quite a few books on Stoic teachings in the last few years and how to understand my mindset and beliefs. Using the knowledge gained from reading these books etc. I decided there and then that whatever this turned out to be, I would face it in a calm and rational manner - no matter what it turned out to be!

A few minutes later the doctor rang again. He started asking when I could get to the Clinic for him to go through the results. I am not usually a forceful person, but I stated, "Doctor, I am on holiday and not back for a week at least, so please spit out whatever it is that I KNOW you do not want to discuss over the phone!!!"

Eventually he explained that there were levels of a certain type in the blood/fluid samples that indicated that there was almost definitely a cancerous body in my neck.

Deep breath Andy!

Once again, I focused my mind and thought, "WHATEVER this is, I will deal with it as necessary."

After finishing the call with the doctor, I discreetly found my wife and said that I needed to tell her something. We asked the grandparents to keep an eye on the kids whilst we shuffled away. I explained my conversation with the doctor and what it possibly meant.

When we got back to the campsite later that day we sat down with my in-laws and explained what all the whispering earlier that day had been about. It was then that we decided that we had to deal with it as a family, so when we got back home after the holiday we sat down with the kids and explained that we had something to say. My wife and I explained calmly that it was very likely that I had a cancer of some sort and that we would keep them informed all the way through whatever happened next.

I was so proud of how my family was dealing with this difficult news.

Over the next few weeks, I was back and forth to the hospital for various scans (I think we had all of them!). We then had a meeting with the consultant whose care we were under, who explained that I had a cancerous lymph gland. He explained that surgery was the best course of action rather than chemo/radiotherapy. He then said I should go straight from there to the BRI Hospital for a pre-op check as I was going to have surgery in the coming weeks!

Stay calm Andy - we can deal with whatever this is!

I had the surgery a week later and was in hospital for a week until they were happy that I could go home. As the doctor had explained, the surgery would result in me having a large wound that would affect the nerves etc that controlled the neck/shoulder area. I was in a lot of pain, but kept reminding myself that this would pass.

After further tests etc it was explained that the lymph gland was the secondary cancer and that it had started somewhere else! Again, more tests and scans which lead to the consultant deciding that I would need surgery to the base of my tongue to remove the cancerous section. It was explained that this could result in a loss of speech and taste.

Again, I decided that I would be able to deal with whatever the outcome was.

So again, I went into the hospital for surgery. I had to be in there at 6 o'clock in the morning ready to go into surgery once the day's schedule was confirmed. I came round after what was a very long surgery (five hours!) to extreme pain and a tube hanging out of my nose!

As before, I thought to myself again and again - this will pass.

I was allowed home after a week after a lot of protesting that home would be better than being in hospital. The pain was so extreme that I had to get some morphine from my GP to help me get through it. A few weeks later I had to have several scans to determine how successful the surgery had been.

An appointment to meet with my consultant came in the post. Once again, I kept reminding myself that I would be able to deal with whatever the outcome was.

The morning of the appointment came and I travelled into Bristol to meet the consultant who said the following:

"Mr Hook, I am pleased to say that you have the all clear! We have successfully removed the cancer from both locations and I am happy to say you are in remission."

Previously, if you had asked me how I would have been after getting news like this, I would have said I would burst into tears! But no - I took it in in a calm, measured way.

Yes, I am in remission and have regular check-ups to keep an eye on any possible changes, as well as trying to cope as well as possible with the pain and discomfort the surgery has left me with. I focus on doing the best I can to get back the full movement in my neck and shoulder, but remind myself of others whose cancer story isn't as straightforward as mine.

I am now getting back to working on my business and looking forward to the future.

There are two things that I would like to share from my experience:

ALWAYS get things checked out if you think something isn't quite right! Nobody knows your body like you, so please do get things checked out as the sooner you spot things, the sooner they can be put right.

Take control of your inner thoughts. You may not be able to change what happens to you, but you can control how you deal with what happens to you!

I will continue to work on getting my neck/shoulder back to as good as it can be, and staying healthy. I would like to thank my wonderful wife, Sarah, as well as my family, friends, doctors and nursing staff for all the care and support I received through this journey. I would also like to thank Ryan Holiday for helping me to find the Stoical learning that allowed me to create the mindset to deal with whatever life throws at me both now and in the future.

ANDREW BOORMAN

Andrew (to his mum) or Andy (to everyone else) is an accountant who is married with kids and spends his spare time walking, binging the latest Netflix series, watching football, volunteering as a charity trustee and walking some more.

Being a lover of numbers, writing a chapter to go into a book is a totally new and different challenge for him, especially as sharing his thoughts has always been difficult.

Writing about his experiences is helping him to become more open with sharing the way he is feeling. By sharing his experiences, he hopes it can help towards ending the stigma around mental health and inspire everyone to be more open about their feelings.

You can find him sharing on the following social media:

https://www.instagram.com/anxiousaccountant/

https://www.linkedin.com/in/andrew-boorman-fcca-7851682a/

https://twitter.com/AndyJBoo

A Journey That Has Been 40 Years in the Making!

I turn 40 this year, but two years ago I wouldn't have thought I would be making it to my next birthday. Up to then most people from the outside looking in would have seen me as a confident, outgoing person who was living a great life. I had a successful career as an accountant, a beautiful wife, three amazing kids, a nice house, etc.

But that was not the truth. I had spent most of my first 38 years on this planet living the life that I thought I should be living. I had been trying to please everyone, both personally and professionally, whilst at times battling with irritable bowel syndrome, sinus issues and tinnitus. I kept things close to my chest. Now this isn't to say that I hadn't enjoyed my life up to that point. But the continuous pressure I had put myself under meant that I spent a lot of time putting on a brave face and defaulting to, "I'm fine." or, "Yes I can do that." or, "No worries." without thinking of the consequences. I didn't want to admit that something was wrong.

Looking back, there were times in my life when I had periods of depression or anxiety. I would feel so guilty about being off work or letting people down that I would use other excuses to avoid things. This meant I distanced myself from people as much as possible, but I would keep that brave face on. Throughout that time, I never really admitted to myself that I had some deep-rooted issues, which meant that the cycle of depression and anxiety continued to build.

Things started to spiral out of control at the start of Summer 2018. I was off work with anxiety and depression for just over 3 weeks. I returned to work having not changed anything: not getting the support I needed, although knew I could get, and still putting that brave face on. I was being told I was doing all the right things by my doctor, but I was not telling them the truth, the whole truth and nothing but the truth.

Fast forward to October 2018 and living the lie was finally catching up with me and my doctor advised me not to go on a family trip to New York. I started to find myself getting more and more depressed and didn't know where to turn. I kept thinking I shouldn't be feeling like this, I should be living my best life, I didn't have anything to be depressed about. The stigma of mental health continued to play on my mind.

A month later I thought I had nowhere to go, so I left a note for my wife and left in the car to kill myself. I was driving around for what felt like forever until I pulled over somewhere near Stroud and tried, but couldn't do it. Luckily, I returned home to be met by my wife and the police. One thing that sticks in my mind is that the police said I was only a moment away from being one of those missing people that the police share on Facebook.

That day, even though I didn't realise it at the time, was the start of my journey of recovery. I didn't know how to tell anyone how I felt and I am still learning every day. But that day meant it was time to accept I had a serious issue with my mental health and things had to change; I needed to be more open. I hated having time off work sick. When my IBS flared up, or my sinuses played up I would struggle into the office put on that brave face. I always felt like I needed to be back at work as soon as I felt even a little bit better.

Now, I would love to be able to tell you as I am writing this that my journey is complete and I am living my best life, but I have to admit I am not there yet. I know it's going to take time, but if you had offered me how I am feeling today, back on that day in 2018, I would have snapped your hand off.

My wife has been my rock for the past two years and I owe her everything, but even now I am still learning how to communicate how I am feeling with her. It's been difficult for her, as I needed time to retrain my default setting that had been with me for 40 years. From that day in 2018, when she squeezed me so tight, I have been working hard to become the all-new, mentally strong me for her and all my family, even with the bumps in the road.

So, my biggest advice to start recovering is acceptance. If you don't accept where you are and are constantly fighting things, then you are always going to be fighting a losing battle. Some days that is easier said than done and you have to find out the things that work for you. Don't let people tell you how you should be feeling, or what you need to do to get better. For someone who always said, "Yes." as I never wanted to upset anyone, I have started to enter the scary territory of saying, "No." This sounds easy, but I still find it difficult to not say, "Yes." on autopilot.

Some things that really helped me early on in my journey were:

Counselling: I had a number of sessions which were really helpful for me to be able to talk about things I would not have wanted to share with anyone I knew.

Reflexology: a relaxing foot (or hand) massage that works on the pressure points in the feet to stimulate and relax the internal organs.

Hypnotherapy: I was sceptical before this, but it isn't like every time my wife clicks her fingers I now cluck like a chicken! The aim is a solution focused hypnotherapy which looks to make you feel more positive about life.

Work-Life Balance: I looked at the time I had in my life and what was important to me: spending time with my family was right up there. So, I changed my working pattern to compress my hours into 4 days and luckily my workplace is flexible so I can swap that around when I need to.

On a more day-to-day basis, I have implemented a number of things during the last 2 years to help with my recovery:

Breathing: this is something that is always there and you can focus on your breathing as a way to distract from thoughts. I have been doing the 4-7-8 breathing technique developed by Dr Weil which is a simple, portable stress antidote.

Calm App: I use this to do my daily calm meditations and sleep stories.

Sharing Memes on Instagram: mainly around supporting people's mental health.

Unfollowing People: those who don't help with my mental health. Mainly on social media, but also in real life if needs be. This included closing down my old Facebook account and opening a new one.

Not looking at my phone in the bedroom: most days.

Getting out of the house: even when I don't feel like it, even if it is just to go for a walk.

And finally, walking: walking and more walking.

One of my biggest anxieties is around my health and being able to enjoy days out and holidays. So much so that I still struggle with this and I had been working on a facing my fears gradual exposure ladder to get to Florida in November 2020. This meant working on exposing myself to a higher level of fear. Unfortunately, the Covid pandemic put a stop to that near the bottom of the ladder, so I am starting that journey again as things start to open back up. My wife and kids managed to escape for a 4-day break in Cornwall but I wasn't ready. In the past this would have impacted me significantly, but I know that I need to do the right thing to keep my journey on track for the long term.

I now know it's ok not to be ok, but still need to work on telling other people that. I know from being in the darkest of places that even though I am not living my 'best' life, it doesn't matter, as being alive to live any life is special, not only to me but for those who I love and who love me.

BRIAN FAKIR

Brian is an advocate of self-care and wellbeing in the community, works actively in his local one and is well respected by them. In Brian's own words, he's getting on a bit now, still thinks he's 18 and wishes he knew back then what he knows now and took action on it. Brian loves his family. He has three children and six grandchildren who keep him busy, plus his extended business family. Brian loves technology and new innovations. He is currently working on podcasting as a venture and has been known to appear on radio occasionally. Brian is a keynote speaker and speaks at many events throughout the UK.

You can contact him on: afreshlysqueezedidea@gmail.com

Message in a Bottle

We either drink or we don't. Those who do may have the capacity to drink more than others in a short space of time. Others may just like a tipple or two at a social gathering and leave it at that.

I've been drinking since I was 15. My introduction to alcohol was much earlier; a small VP Sherry with my Christmas dinner, or on New Year's Eve to ring the New Year in.

I smoked the odd cigarette too. My parents smoked and it was easy to pinch one or two from their packets; each would blame the other. My mum wasn't good at knowing how much was left in anything. I was later able to buy ten No6 from the chip shop round the corner. In those days being underage never seemed to be a problem.

A schoolteacher noticed that I had some athletic promise after I outshone everyone else in a sponsored marathon, raising much needed money to purchase the first school minibus. I was used to being chased so could run forever! I gave up cigarettes and took up athletics and cross-country running; I represented the school at many championship meetings.

My first venture into a pub was on a school field trip in the Brecon Beacons during my Duke of Edinburgh's Award sessions. It was the norm to go out for a beer on these trips, apparently. The teacher asked us what we would like before he went to the bar. When it came to my turn, I ordered a pint and, in my naivety, said, "Please, Sir." All eyes were on me in the pub. He quietly came around to me and whispered, "When we are in a pub, I am John, ok?" I said, "Ok, got it, sorry Sir… Uh, I mean John."

Socialising became the norm; going to pubs and on nights out. I was 16, earning from my job and becoming an adult. On a Friday night I'd meet in the pub with mates, play darts and have a real good time. Then on Saturday night it was glad rags on and into town.

In our youth, alcohol played a large part in our lives; it's how we were social with one another. We were all going out, having a good time. I honestly cannot remember anyone who ever said to me, "I do not drink." We all did!

Mum and Dad drank very little. The sideboard had all the remnants of Christmas purchases; VP Sherry, Bell Whisky, the yellow Advocaat for Snowballs, Martini or Cinzano, a single bottle of Blue Nun, Navy Rum and, if they splashed out, a Remy Martin.

Never, ever did I hear, "Let's have a drink with our tea." Lots of the families I knew would go to the 'Offy' (off licence) and buy a flagon if they did not go out on a Friday.

There were no alcoholics - they were the homeless who sat in parks with brown bags and shouted at you, when you walked past, in their prose. The others were drinkers or boozers because they were in control… or were they?

What changed? Society, socialising, wine…

And my attitude to it.

It was probably in the 80's when buying wine from a supermarket to drink at home became the norm. Being able to buy cases of beer back then, like you can now, was a novelty. Alcohol to consume at home became affordable. I developed a taste for red wine and it seemed to like me too. Well, my wallet at least.

Others would agree that I am not a big drinker. I have been out with big drinkers; what they consume and the speed they consume it is something I tried but could not keep up with. I have been with reformed alcoholics and drug addicts who told me stories of their typical days. These were respectable people with responsibilities. Some still are, they have reformed and kicked their habit. Others have not made it that far.

At work schmoozing clients at lunches, functions and events, as well as doing my own daily work, invariably involved drinking.

Then home and drink some more.

2004: single and with no responsibilities, I joined a social group of men, mainly rugby fans, to go out and meet new people. I took my freedom seriously. I was out 7 full days a week constantly socialising, gym every day, kickboxing and running. Then off out drinking again, back to my apartment and more drinking. This was my norm.

Each time I would bid farewell to the folk I was with and go home and drink some more, a lot more. That continued for an awfully long time and as time went on it became less going out and more drinking at home every evening.

In 2012, now in a long-term relationship, I woke in the middle of the night with the most horrendous pain I had ever encountered. Convinced I was in heart failure, I was crawling on the bedroom floor in agony. I was blue lighted to hospital and spent overnight on a morphine drip. My now-wife was convinced I was dying.

The diagnosis was a damaged gall bladder. I was not having any of it, no surgery thanks. I was going to change my lifestyle. I attributed the gallstones to bad food choices and amended my diet accordingly: no more processed foods or networking hotel breakfasts (4 days a week consistently). Cut out drinking? Uh no, this has nothing to do with drinking. It's food related!

I started self-managing my pain and discomfort and convincing myself my gallbladder would repair itself through healthy food choices. At one point I was given some Co-codamol by a relative to help with the pain, you know how the elderly stockpile prescriptions. I took some and it helped. On one occasion I could feel a twinge and knew it was coming, so I had a few drinks and had a bath, took two pills. Got out, laid on the bed and passed out… blinkin' hot baths.

At a networking event I felt pain coming on. My nutritionist friend noticed as I looked pasty and was sweating. She asked if I was ok; I wasn't to be honest. She saw the packet of Co-codamol on the table and asked me if I'd taken any.

"Yeah, I just took two before the breakfast." She threw the packet across the table, ushered me out of the room, got me drinking copious amounts of water and told me that just one tablet had the power to knock a horse out and to stop taking them.

*Readers please note: *never, ever* take anything that's not been prescribed for *you*.*

There began the journey of healthy eating and unhealthy drinking because I was still convinced that the two were unrelated.

I continued to self-manage the pain. My health was being restored but, alas, I was not getting any better. One morning in late 2018 I got up as normal, came out of the bathroom, my wife looked at me and said, "Have you seen yourself?" … "What do you mean?" … "You're yellow," she said, "you look jaundiced, phone the doctor now."

After the GP sent me for blood tests, he implored me to remove the gall bladder or I would have this pain for the rest of my life and it could even be fatal if left. I had further tests and scans and made the decision to have surgery, which frightened the pants off me.

If you have watched Casualty, or hospital programmes in general, you can picture the scene. The consultant spent an age on one spot, going back and forth for what seemed like an eternity. His head moved in different angles and his expression changed as he looked at the image.

I had to see another consultant and, here came the hammer blow, a liver specialist. That only meant one thing; my persistent drinking had finally caught up with me. I am done for. The scan showed a slight sclerosis of the liver. I asked the consultant, "Slight? That's not bad then, is it?" … "No, but it's not good either. It could get worse and explains your jaundice, along with the gall bladder problem. You must act now."

I announced in that room, Jan 31st 2019, that I would not touch another drop of alcohol.

Why do I remember that date so well? There is a tournament called the Six Nations Rugby, which involves a lot of socialising and drinking; celebrating or commiserating for 8 weekends. With a sense of irony, I congratulated the consultant on delivering the news on the eve of this tournament. His timing was impeccable.

I am committed to doing this and I'm doing it today, because I am not ready to die… well not this way.

6 months later I had the op. Two consultants believed the gall bladder problem masked the liver and there was nothing wrong with it, while the third consultant was not entirely convinced and would not discharge me.

I have mostly kept my alcohol-free lifestyle up. I have met others who have given up too. One person in particular; she was 23 and she told me that her university time was 3 years of binge drinking and she'd just been diagnosed with liver disease and if she didn't stop now her life would be over, at 23…

Feb 5th, 2020, the eve of the Six Nations. 12 months, 365 days later. I decided that I can do it and probably will do it again. We celebrated with a drink - a glass of wine. To be honest, it tasted awful and I left it at that. I drink occasionally, not at the levels or style that I would have in the past. If we go out socially now, it's a soft drink or low alcohol beer regime.

Was I an alcoholic? I may have been in others' eyes. I knew alcoholics and then again, I knew ones I did not realise were as well.

Was I addicted? Possibly. I took every opportunity to go for a drink or have one, I enjoyed the taste of red wine and I drank a lot of it. Marks and Spencer do the 25% off for six bottles offer and I would be in there every 2 or 3 days and I would be the one consuming the majority of it.

Was I a drunk? I would fall asleep, tipping a full glass over myself or, more often, kicking one over on the carpet. The soppy, silly drunk if anything, probably a bit argumentative sometimes, but I never hurt or abused anyone, *ever*. The only hurt I caused was to my wife's constant wish that I would stop drinking so much. The liver scan, which she witnessed, hurt her a lot. It was her 'I told you so' moment - the biggest upset.

Was I hiding from my problems? I'd like to say no...

I really, really enjoyed drinking: fact.

There are people reading this right now who sail through life drinking and it never affects them. Mothers, fathers, sons and daughters who rely on alcohol as a crutch or drink just because they enjoy it. Our brains trick us about what we think we've consumed. Look at a large wine glass: two of those is literally a bottle of wine and if you're having a couple of people around for an evening it's easy to get through three or four bottles.

It's not until a trigger health problem forces someone into a thought process like mine, of maybe I have been over doing it on the alcohol. Because rest assured, if it hadn't happened to me, I would still be drinking loads.

If you drink a lot please, please go and have a blood test with your GP. It might just be a lifesaver... it saved mine!

CHRIS GARVEY

Chris Garvey, husband, father and a true advocate of a 'bounce back lifestyle'. An international speaker, entrepreneur, coach and author; empowering clients from around the globe to live a life full of love, health and wellbeing.

He is the founder and CEO of Habitual, a health and wellbeing organisation providing clients with a platform to create lasting health change.

In a previous life he was a teacher, ultra-endurance athlete and had ambitions of being the oldest person to complete a marathon, that was until things changed. He'd like to share his story with you. Is that okay?

https://www.habitual.club

chris@habitual.club

Make Life Great Again

My life is great. As I write this, I sit with a cup of coffee looking out upon the waters in Repulse Bay; a beautiful beach on the south coast of Hong Kong. It's Monday, my day off. This morning I kissed my son and my wife goodbye as the sun came up and set off with my breakfast, laptop and notebooks. I have just finished hiking over the many peaks and around the many reservoirs the island has to offer. This afternoon I'm meeting a good friend. Right now, I am right where I want to be, doing what I love. My life is great.

But it wasn't always this way.

Growing up, my life was great. You would find me playing down the field with friends, coming in only for food and when that sad moment came each day, indicated by the street lights coming on. I had a happy childhood. I studied a little, I played a lot and I did the things that brought me joy. Always encouraged by my parents; they showed me love, understanding and unconditional regard. I would say, all a boy could ever want. One could say my life was great.

All things considered, my education was great. At 10 years old, Mr. Green became my first male teacher and role model; an enigmatic individual, always with a smile and looking at home in his tracksuit. Maybe it's what I want to remember, but it seemed each day was a day of sport and a little maths, both made so much fun by Mr. Green. I knew from the age of 11 that I wanted to play sport, wear tracksuits and get paid for it; I was going to be a physical education teacher. From this moment on my career path was set. I knew what I needed to study and had a purpose. My education was great.

Early adulthood, on the whole, was great. As I experienced the realities of adult life I made mistakes, I had my share of upsets and no doubt upset others. Throughout, my teaching provided me with a lifestyle; a chance to travel and a chance to gain perspective on the world. Teaching brought me to three major cities and two countries. I moved out of my childhood home in Birmingham to be with my soon to be wife in London, before settling in Hong Kong where my mind was to be opened to a whole new world of experiences. Being an adult was great.

Teaching was my life for 11 glorious years until 2015, when I left the profession to continue to explore what brings me joy. With the love and support of my wife, I embarked on a Masters in Applied Psychology and set up a business providing health consulting, offering online and in person services from fitness, nutrition and health coaching. Learning was great.

The business moved forward quickly. I was developing a complete online mental, physical and social well-being platform and I had a pilot program lined up for a number of international schools. There was interest, there was demand, schools really wanted to support their staff and students. Business was going great.

Outside education and business, I had continued to play. Hong Kong opened up a brand new playground. A wonderful opportunity to coach the Hong Kong Women's rugby team opened up for me and Ultra endurance events became available with a new location and finances. Events ranged from a solo cycling event from Hong Kong to Vietnam, a 14-day ride through 13 peaks and 2500km of Japan, to a 24-hour group deadlifting event to lift one million kilos. I continued to work, play and challenge myself mentally and physically.

In December 2018 I embarked on one of the biggest challenges to date. I was invited to compete in the Spartan World Championships in Iceland. A 24-hour obstacle race in sub-zero temperatures, 5 hours of daylight and no fixed distance. This was the ultimate playground. My life was great, my business was thriving, the birth of my first child was providing love, joy and well-being, my relationship with my wife was strong. Life was great.

But things were about to go drastically downhill…

The years following the Spartan World Championships, it was clear that my well-being platform would need to be pulled. One developer had run off to join the Ukrainian army, leaving me with an unfinished platform. The new developer's costs were spiralling and my savings were almost gone. Sports coaching and supply work had completely dried up due to COVID. My vision was slipping away and my company was close to broke. Life was getting challenging.

It's okay, I still have my health?

A lifetime of adventure had resulted in a little wear and tear on my left hip. In August 2019, I went in for routine surgery to prevent further damage to my femur and pelvis. Andy Murray, the British tennis player, had the same operation and his quick return to sport made me confident I would back playing, soon enough.

Post-operation, the surgeon and anaesthetist were bedside; as they rolled a little spiky ball down my leg, my right side was fine, feeling was back and I could move as normal, but there was something not right on my left side. No matter what they did or what I tried, I was unable to feel anything below the hip. I brushed this off in a postoperative haze, but after 3 days and no return of feeling it dawned on me something was seriously wrong.

It's okay, I still have my family?

After release from hospital with a lot of painkillers and a strong leg brace, it was not long before the discomfort and sleepless nights had resulted in my wife sleeping in the next room with my newborn son. I hit an all-time low. I couldn't provide, carry or care for my wife or my son and the strain was showing on our relationship. Life was not good.

Left alone with my thoughts, I contemplated the money I had lost, the people I had let down, a wife and child whom I could not be trusted to care for and contemplated the potential of never being able to walk again. Laying there on my own I had plenty of time to think and the thought I kept coming back to was 'maybe'. Maybe I would stay broke, maybe I would never walk again, maybe I would not be able to care for my son. Maybe. I broke down and sobbed; I felt powerless, afraid and alone.

Maybe it did not have to be this way.

Victor Frankl wrote, 'Between stimulus and response, there is a space. In that space lies our freedom and our power to choose our response. In our response lies our growth and our happiness.' I don't believe in 'aha' moments, but I do believe that life is reflected by the load we are willing to carry and the skills we learn to lighten the load. I had allowed myself to see all that was wrong; maybe I could deal with this.

I had been challenged before; I had actively sought out challenges before. This challenge was not one I had signed up for, but it was the one I was in. I was now in the biggest challenge of my life. I had a choice to come to terms with the new situation so I could enjoy a future of love, a future of joy and a future of fulfilment for myself and those whom are close to me, or choose to lie there and cry.

Everything I had ever done had prepared me for this moment. I had to look back with acceptance; there was nothing that could be changed. I had to look forward with hope, optimism and a plan of what is yet to come. I had to once again live for this moment right now, working with what I could control and let go of what I could not.

Right now.

Right now, 14 months post-operation, my leg is operating at 50 percent. I am still unable to contract part of my quad but I can walk, jog very slowly and I can carry my growing son. I have my health.

Right now, I'm the husband of an independent, loving and supportive wife and father of a lively and happy young son, with one on the way. I have my family.

Right now, I am coaching. My business is growing again and I await potential governmental grants to kickstart the platform. My goals have not changed but the approach and timelines have. I have my purpose.

As I finish my second cup of coffee, I reflect on the people I am blessed to have in my life: those whom I love and love me back. I reflect on what I am able to do. Yes, there are difficulties and challenges. But you could say I am in a good place, you could say I am at peace and 'maybe' you can be too.

DANNY LLOYD

I am a former construction coordinator/design engineer. I have anti phospholipid syndrome (APS), which caused two strokes, kidney damage and adrenal insufficiency.

Bodybuilding's played a huge part in my life. I've practiced jujitsu, judo and road cycling. I became a yoga practitioner, which was the start of my self-discovery journey. The greatest and most noticeable changes however have come from T'ai Chi practice.

I'm a founding member of 'The Brain Injury Cafe Bristol' a peer group for anyone affected by a brain injury.

I've become a 'Stroke Ambassador' for the Stroke Association and spoke about my experiences at the international congress for APS in Manchester.

https://www.facebook.com/groups/975365819241524/

https://www.instagram.com/the.reset.button/

Email: dlloydy1973@gmail.com

Bit of a Worry

The journey to being me.

Life:

At school, despite having lots of friends and being fairly intelligent, I lacked confidence. I remember there being a general undercurrent of fear that something was going to go wrong. I don't know why, or when it started. I know I was quite sensitive as a child. I really didn't like the feeling, yet had no clue as to what it was or why it was there. I ignored it, smiled, carried on and put up with it. I convinced myself it was just how I was.

The first time I can remember it physically affecting me was around the time I left school and embarked on my working life.

Like many, I fell onto my career path, not really knowing what I wanted to do. I decided on a trainee civil engineering position because I liked technical drawing. The position consisted of 4 days of work, 1 day and 1 evening at college. I felt I had to forge a career and that having 'just a job' was never a choice.

1 week after starting, I had a prearranged 2-week holiday with my parents and sister. The long-planned trip was our first to Canada visiting family.

I remember the holiday for the wrong reasons. I had nausea and sickness almost immediately on arriving, which persisted for the majority of the 2 weeks.

Back in the UK life carried on. I continued to play rugby, which I began playing in secondary school, together with the associated social events that went with it. Well that was the intention anyway.

However, a pattern became apparent. A night out would be arranged, I'd look forward to it, talk about it, then about an hour before leaving I'd feel ill. My stomach would churn, I'd feel nauseous, then I'd throw up. This happened on almost every occasion and when it did, I would cancel going and feel an instant relief. Until about 30 minutes after everyone had gone, when I'd feel I was missing out; guilty, angry and frustrated at myself for being this way. I didn't understand, it just happened.

I got used to the feeling and learned to hide it quite well, gradually I accepted it was just how I was. I hated the feeling.

Through rugby I'd started strength training aged around 15. I realised after a few years that I enjoyed the gym training more than I did playing rugby. I decided I wasn't going back the following season. A bonus being, no more socials!

I believed that how I felt would go as my circumstances had changed, it didn't happen of course. Any social event brought about the same reaction. I kept this all to myself for many years; I felt embarrassed, confused, frustrated and quite pathetic. I thought I'd outgrow it at some point down the line.

Bodybuilding:

I intensified my gym lifestyle as I was starting to see results from my efforts. Bodybuilding had become my obsession, my go to, my church. It was the one thing I had control over and it was something that paid you back for the effort you put in. You can't buy that in any shop and that's what made me tick. The amount of effort and dedication put in was directly displayed in how you looked. Additionally, I met what were to become my dearest, closest friends during the years of gym training.

Things started to get serious when I decided to put my efforts on display and entered a bodybuilding contest. This took me about as far out of my comfort zone as I could get. I applied myself to the task: if I was doing it, I had to be the absolute best I could be. No excuses, no blaming anyone, it was all on me.

I had the date set and work started. The months, weeks, then days ticked by as the calories reduced. If you haven't experienced dieting whilst weight training consistently, together with doing daily cardio...don't!

With a few weeks to go I realised I had to put together a piece of posing music and choreograph a routine. I surprised myself in this regard. I came up with a cobbled together routine, stolen pretty much from a professional bodybuilder's guest appearance I had watched.

Competition day came around, bringing my all too familiar anxious feelings with it. I hadn't considered this aspect, only that I knew I'd be nervous. My saviour came in the fact that I was exhausted and very hungry. A pizza was the reward waiting on the other side. I got to the point where I just wanted it to be over.

I competed, enjoyed the attention while it lasted and looked forward to taking the next step as a competitive bodybuilder.

Underneath all of this and despite how I now looked, I still had very little confidence and generally felt anxious half of the time. I told myself I was 'just a worrier', it was part of my personality and made me, me.

Chronic Illness:

After a brief break from the gym and a lot of (over) eating I returned to my usual routine of working, training, eating and sleeping. However, very quickly, things seemed such hard work.

For a while I was sure I felt this way because of the competition. I was tired all the time no matter how much rest I had. I carried on thinking it would pass, however, things got weird!

Initially, I noticed myself being physically restless. This was particularly noticeable at my place of work. I was now employed by a national housebuilder as a junior engineer. My role included producing drawings on a large drawing board using ink pens, which I started to drop and now struggled to keep hold of. It was getting worse too.

I ignored it, thinking it would pass. It didn't. I started to open/close my hands constantly, tap my feet and keep moving my legs around. This was getting worse and more noticeable.

I had some appointments with my doctor about it, however, I wasn't taken seriously and everything was attributed to my bodybuilding lifestyle and overdoing things. I knew something wasn't right though.

By now my symptoms were obvious, I literally couldn't keep still. I added involuntary facial movements to the party, which included a feeling of my tongue being too big for my mouth!

I made yet another doctor's appointment. Initially it felt like I was going to be treated the same way as before, however I think my strange movement/fidgetiness was noticed so having my blood pressure taken was 'offered', I felt mainly to shut me up.

I've never forgotten the doctor's confused/stunned face on seeing the result. It was double-checked and the result was the same. It was very high. The doctor informed me that she would make some enquiries and get back to me later that day if necessary.

I headed straight off to work for another day of fidgeting, dropping things and trying to act as though nothing was going on.

Around 3pm the manager of the department received a phone call which he was transferring to me. To add some context this was 1995, the mobile phone didn't exist, non-work related phone calls just didn't happen unless it was very important.

I answered the call, feeling very self-conscious as I knew the team would be listening in… I'm unsure of the majority of the conversation, apart from that I needed to go back to the doctors to have my BP rechecked. "Of course," I replied, "I'll come straight after work so it will probably be around 5:45pm because of the traffic." They replied, "No, you need to come now!"

Now slightly panicked, I agreed, cleared it with my boss and headed back to the doctors.

At the doctors I was called through, my BP was rechecked and the result was the same as earlier that day. I was given a letter and instructions to go directly to an assessment ward at the local hospital. "This is weird," I thought.

I was admitted and things seemed to get serious. I had so many medical checks, blood tests and more unusual assessments. These included various scans, an EEG (brain electrical activity), a kidney biopsy, lumbar punctures and even a session in a film recording room where my strange face and body movements were filmed.

Following admission my symptoms worsened and gradually I lost the ability to speak. I had virtually no fine motor control of my hands, so couldn't write, essentially my basic forms of communication were gone. The strange thing was at no point did I feel worried; however, I was very frustrated and confused.

It felt like an age to get any type of explanation as to what was going on. Eventually, I was diagnosed as having something called antiphospholipid syndrome - APS for short.

APS, in simple terms, is an autoimmune condition whereby the blood becomes 'sticky', clots form and it then cannot circulate properly.

It transpired I'd experienced a small stroke (I have a dead area of my brain!) and sustained kidney damage. I had severe fatigue and I couldn't speak without slurring really badly when I was able to form words properly.

There is no cure for APS, however it is treatable...fortunately.

The next few weeks/months really dragged as nothing much was changing. I was exhausted, frustrated and had nothing to do every day, so I walked.

I was waking early, so the days felt even longer. My walks were as long as I could manage. However, this brought its own stress. I had to be sure I could make it back before being too exhausted and I had to find times/places where I could avoid meeting people, especially anyone who knew me.

My biggest fear now was someone talking to me as I could not speak to answer them. This made me rather paranoid. I avoided everyone outside of my close group of friends and immediate family.

Getting Back To 'Normal':

Over time my speech slowly returned and the fatigue gradually reduced. I returned to work in a phased process. My employer was very accommodating and understanding, which helped a lot.

My real drive, however, was to get back to the gym, to my friends and to pick up where I left off, or so I thought.

Sadly, it wasn't to be and no matter how much I convinced myself it could be, I realised that part of my life would never be the same again.

So instead of giving myself time to come to terms with this, I decided to start something new and ignored my 'new' medical condition. Despite being on anticoagulant medication, which put me at an increased risk of bleeding, I joined a combat Jujitsu club and I loved it. I attended a judo club for several years as a child and it was surprising how quite a lot felt natural early on. I reassured myself it was a good idea by cherry picking the medical advice given to me.

A doctor informed me that contact sports were not an option open to me, however, I'd also been advised I shouldn't wrap myself up in cotton wool… So, I chose to focus on this aspect!

I was very, very lucky. I practiced regularly for roughly 9 years and only really suffered bruises and numerous cuts. These were more a cause of frustration as I was spending more and more time sitting out of sessions, partway through, to stop myself bleeding over everything and everyone.

It was a ridiculous situation and deep down I knew it. A big realisation came during a boxing sparring session with my long-time friend and training partner. I got hit on the cheek just below my eye and my skin split. It took an age to stop and even our experienced instructor looked concerned. My friend was apologetic and felt bad. It was sparring after all. The cut healed; it was fine. What this did was made me think about the real risks. What if I'd been seriously hurt or had an internal bleed? That would be on someone else's conscience. Not only was I at risk, I was putting others in a position where they unknowingly could be made to feel responsible for causing me a serious injury, or worse.

I left the club straight away, however I did continue practicing judo as it carried a lesser risk, as I saw it.

Underneath all of this my personal life was far from good. I had children relatively young and I was always doing the right thing in terms of what I thought was my responsibility to my family - and I was, of course, more than happy to.

However, this came crashing down when I separated from my long since ex-partner. Instantly I found myself labelled public enemy number one. I had to take matters to a family court to ensure contact with the children was maintained which, in my view, was completely unnecessary.

I moved on, changed jobs, where I lived and met a new partner.

At first things were great, or so I thought. Over time I gradually stopped the things I enjoyed, the things that made me who I was, to suit my partner. This also included getting married 18 months after the first planned wedding was cancelled at short notice!

My ex eventually decided to leave, she moved out and into a rented shared house for a year! I waited, unable to move on. I felt pathetic and frustrated.

I was in a downhill negative spiral, not that I realised it for a while. Over time I'd slowly lost my identity, despite hiding it, or so I thought, from the world with a standard, "I'm alright thanks." response to pretty much anything. The anxiety that I'd squashed was showing itself all the time. I was becoming obsessive with day-to-day things and depressed. I carried this for a long time, often berating myself, struggling to understand why I felt the way I did and believing I should 'snap out of it'. I think I had a 'nervous breakdown' at some point as things got so bad. I was determined now more than ever to understand and resolve whatever it was, regardless of others. This was for myself. I was determined to turn my 'breakdown' into a 'breakthrough'.

I was fortunate that I was in a position where I had the resources to research and try out numerous therapies, some of which were odd, some very helpful and made sense in explaining that what I experienced was an 'overcooked' natural reaction. Something was working and it was changing me for the better.

I'm certain that all of this was preparing me for what was coming around the corner, not so far into the future, where I would need a solid, stable and determined mindset to initially survive and then thrive in life as I am now.

For me, learning to understand what anxiety is and why it happens started a shift. Realising it's a natural process that is overreacting to everyday events allowed me to start to accept it.

My close friends and family were superb throughout it all and still are; always there to listen, never judging or telling me their opinions although no doubt they would have had them! I like to think I'm now in a position to help others should it ever be needed.

Around 6 years ago I met my fantastic partner Emma. From the start it was clear we'd lived very similar lives, we have a lot of shared values and a lot in common, including a brain injury!

It sounds terrible, whereas in reality it really works!

DANNY MATTHEWS

From running a tattoo shop at 18 to becoming the first mortgage advisor to digitise the mortgage application process, Danny Matthews has a natural story-telling ability that he now uses to solve real business problems with creative design and branding through his company Danny&co. and his trademark process Brand Confidence®.

Danny was chosen as one of Business Insider's '42Under42'. He is also a speaker and lecturer on the business of creativity and has been featured in places like the Huffington Post, Financial Times and the FSB's First Voice.

You can find out more about the Danny and the studio by visiting:

https://www.dannyand.co

https://www.linkedin.com/in/theactualdanny/

The Illusion of Happiness

A blessing and a curse. A double-edged sword. Whatever you want to call it, for me it just felt like the end. The end of my career, marriage and what was left of any friendships I had.

This is what happens when you're given an offer you can't refuse - and you refuse it.

I *still* can't put into words what comes next, so I find myself in a permanent paradox of hoping that nobody goes through the same thing and also understanding that it was the catalyst for me becoming truly happy.

My story begins in childhood. Reminisce with me for a minute and imagine sketchbooks piled up in the corner of the bedroom; pencils, felt-tip pens, the shavings of pencils everywhere and marks on the carpet of my bedroom from the pencil lead. I was always creative. I think we all were at one time in our early lives.

Whether it was drawing a new model of a car, recreating my favourite game characters and superheroes or just letting it flow, letting just about anything land on the page. That was, until the serious stuff came along and I had to take SATS or GCSE exams. Then all of a sudden art, design, graphics were a no-go when deciding on your career choice.

Growing up on blues music, Japanese animated movies and gaming, I was utterly romantic about what I wanted to do when I left school. Living in Japan and creating the characters and voices for cartoons was the dream. Sounds wild, but it didn't feel like it back then. It was a dream that slowly faded as I grew into a young adult and allowed the sensible, responsible voices to tell me what kind of path was suitable for me out in the 'real world'.

I still haven't been to Japan, but I kept a glimmer of creativity and subtly weaved my skill throughout the supposed 'real jobs' until the perfect opportunity presented itself, which is where I stopped chasing cash and took a chance on my dream. All I wanted was to say, "I am a designer and I LOVE my job."

Instead, I cut my teeth on the hard stuff. Market trading, knocking doors, you name it - I did it. Soul destroying, ridiculously well-paid jobs. The whole experience must have sent me into a rebellion. Over the next few years, I worked as a retail assistant in an alternative clothing shop with a piercing studio, working my way up to supervisor and going between two stores. And of course, I had to fit in, so I stretched my earlobes with bamboo horns, pierced both my nipples, up-skilled to a tattoo artist and set up a tattoo parlour in the heart of the Midlands, Birmingham.

Tattoo culture pre-2010 wasn't what it is now; a trendy form of expression. It was a gateway for 'other business' to take place. When I met my wife Caroline, I ruffled a few feathers and was forced to move on, but the one thing I really loved about my time at the shop was hearing the stories. I know it now as semiotics; how meaning is created and communicated through signs and symbols, but the deep-rooted reasoning behind why someone would permanently brand their skin with a symbol or piece of art was fascinating.

Leaving the shop was tough. It wasn't only great money and paid in cash, I was so close to the kind of career I wanted. So, I started to try and find ways to continue doing something creative, but it needed more legitimacy and less - you know - other stuff. I was in a relationship now and living with Caroline's parents.

It was time to grow up.

I started the process of building a business plan for an eco-friendly print and design business called 'Eco-print'. It made perfect sense because the government was talking a lot about sustainable forestry (yes, it was even a thing back then) and I saw an opportunity to start designing business stationery and print marketing materials. What I didn't expect was being asked to contribute half of the funding to start the business - I thought it was a loan. An industrial grade, basic printer was going to set me back a minimum of £7,000. Where was a 19-year-old kid supposed to get that kind of money?

A dream short lived and I was forced back into sensibly working in offices, doing admin jobs until I became an account manager for a health insurance agent. I hit the big time. I mean, he frequently hit the big time - I saw the commission statements. All this insurance and financial services stuff looked like something I could really get into. I hadn't seen a paycheck like that since knocking doors and all he seemed to do was take the appointments from the telesales person and come back with an application. I wanted some of that.

Creativity went out of the window along with the bamboo horns and the nipple bars and I eventually got what I wanted; running an insurance and mortgage brokerage of my own.

Until around 2017 it was predominantly a face-to-face industry. I would travel to see a prospect to discuss their needs, travel back to the office, spend hours researching the market and advising them on their options. If they accepted my recommendation, I would submit an application and it was great if it was accepted as it meant that the likelihood of me being paid was a little bit higher. If not, I had to start all over again and at this point get paid nothing.

It was inefficient and the experience from a customer and an adviser point of view was decades out of date. After hundreds of conversations with officials and representatives of banks, lawyers and the industry regulators, I took the opportunity to build and market a proof of concept called 'Mortgy Digital Mortgages' and became the first mortgage adviser to digitise the process of obtaining client information and recommending a mortgage.

It was the perfect segue and propelled me into what became my first branding and digital design project to be led completely by me. I was in at the deep end and it felt incredible. I knew it would work - my proof of concept took £1.3 million of applications and it was a 'botch job'. I met CEO's of banks and technologists working to change the world of banking. I was travelling to London at 4am, returning home sometimes at nearly midnight. I experienced business like business is meant to be.

I was asked to build the same concept, but for real. It was going to help a small company bid for a multi-billion-pound contract by allowing them to take 100 times more business for what was a really small investment. On successful completion I would be Chief Digital Officer of one of the most successful brokers in London, have an impressive 6-figure salary, bonus, expenses - for a lot of people, this was the dream. It felt like I should have been the happiest man alive. This was the offer I couldn't refuse.

They won the contract.

I woke up at the normal time - 4am - but I was travelling from Digbeth Coach Station in Birmingham as we had been staying with Caroline's dad who had just been diagnosed with lung cancer. It didn't make sense to be 90 miles away in the Cotswolds when I could be working from anywhere. So, I tucked my laptop into my backpack, grabbed a snack and a can of ginger beer for the journey and got on my way.

If you've ever travelled to Digbeth, even though it's right on the edge of town, most of the parking is short stay and I needed it for up to 12 hours. Not knowing any of this beforehand, I drove around for 20 minutes trying to find a parking space that didn't mean a 10-minute walk to the coach, because then I'd be late for my departure. And I *was* late - so I ran.

When I got to London, Victoria I grabbed my usual coffee from the Starbucks on the corner as I walked to the tube station and psyched myself up for the biggest meeting of my life. Little old me and a bit of creativity helping a small mortgage broker basically dominate an entire section of the market.

Then it hit me.

I was barely 50 yards from the London office when I brushed myself down and felt a dampness on the back of my shirt and trousers. As I moved my hands upward to decipher where the liquid was coming from, I realised it was my backpack. Ginger beer!

I froze and my entire body went into shock, firing adrenaline all over, pins and needles, sweating. My instinct said to call Cal, my wife. We've been through so much together and she had been a rock through her dad's diagnosis, still enabling me to take a huge risk with this venture, so naturally she was the first person I thought of. I grabbed my phone and tapped her name, shaking uncontrollably.

Something was happening to me.

She picked up the phone and as she went to speak, I lost feeling from the waist down and fell to the ground, knees first. As Cal gave me a 'time out' talk and I started to pull myself together, three people who had been spectating came over to see if I was ok.

That's when I decided that the offer I couldn't refuse, wasn't worthy of me.

I didn't know what I was going to do. I had no idea what would happen to me when I went home to tell my Cal that after all of the hard work and sacrifice, our life - in fact - wasn't going to change for the better.

All I knew was that I was done chasing the money. Done working for 'the man'. The only thing I continued after this experience was, surprisingly, my occasional enjoyment of a nice cold ginger beer.

My little existential crisis led me full circle. Creativity, art, design. And on the morning of my 30th birthday, at the dining table of my friend's house where we were staying (yes, we moved again), my life's journey of finding happiness really began.

Fast forward a little to you reading this; I'm standing at my home office desk, the owner of a creative design and branding studio where we have the pleasure of helping new brands get into the right hands and add new life to old brands. I also regularly guest lecture and help new and upcoming designers and creatives use their skill in the real world; starting businesses or giving them their dream job.

People still ask me about my proof of concept, Mortgy, and what happened. To keep it short I say, "I sold it," but if you're reading this now you know the whole story and how I found true happiness.

For fun, I sometimes say that I've found the thing I would do for free, but also found a way to trick people into paying me for it. There's some truth to that, but what I have come to realise is that design is my skill and it's what you now know about me from my story that adds real value to what I do.

How I learned to communicate with a cold market knocking doors, to respect diversity, that tattoos aren't just a statement but they hold powerful stories, how every single one of us is capable of amazing things if we put ourselves in a position to receive them and how - above all - design is for life and you can make your life whatever you want it to be.

My name is Danny Matthews. I am a designer and I LOVE my job.

———

DARREN MATTHEWS

Darren is a loving father, mechanical engineer and former Tae Kwon Do instructor who has lived in Bath/Bristol all of his life. The majority of his early years were spent believing he possessed superhuman powers and despite numerous attempts to prove this theory (and subsequent visits to A&E), it wasn't actually the case. However, he has learned in the last few years that it's impossible to be mentally invincible and deployed many strategies to keep himself happy and healthy - something he is happy to share with you.

You can contact Darren through Discover Your Bounce.

Anxiety

Firstly, I would like to point out that I have never written a book or contributed anything to be compiled into a book. Therefore, this is both a surprise that people would like to hear my story and indeed a privilege and honour that this might help others.

I should probably start off by saying a few things about me, who I am and the journey of my life (so far). I am a 46-year-old man who has been married and divorced twice. I have two gorgeous grown up children that I am very proud of and an adorable retired racing greyhound called Boris. I have quite a busy job in sales and, in my spare time, like to keep active and physically challenge myself. I have completed quite a few running events during my life (distance and obstacle) as well achieving a 3rd Dan Black Belt in Tae Kwon Do. I try to keep busy and enjoy trying new experiences and seeing new things. I have recently taken up off-road cycling and enjoy visiting locations I have never been to before. Last year, I cycled to the Gower with a very good friend of mine and camped near the beach – such a great experience. Like most people, I have had my fair share of successes and knocks in life.

I have always been a happy-go-lucky individual, with an extroverted personality, who loves socialising, trying new things and meeting new people. However, following a significant life event last year, I found myself grappling with a new type of challenge that I had never encountered before... poor mental health. This has led me to suffer with anxiety and depression, which impacted many aspects of my working and social life. Where I used to be mostly brimming with confidence, I would at times find myself feeling nervous, doubting my ability and questioning whether I could achieve even the most basic of tasks. It took me a few months to recognise what was actually going on, but I had started to spiral downwards and I didn't like how I was feeling, nor did I feel in control of my emotions. For me, it took the form of a racing heart and knots in my stomach that would make me want to run away (and hide somewhere safe).

It is at times like these when the importance of your friends and family come to the forefront. Also, being open and talking about how you are feeling – something I am not naturally very good at. I am incredibly lucky to have a supportive, loving network of people who care about me – this was a key factor in putting me on the right path. My sister, Nicky Marshall (who fortunately happens to be a health and wellbeing coach/mentor), helped me to create a 'get better' plan, which was the turning point I so desperately needed. This allowed me to take back control of my mental health and steer it in a more positive direction.

So, what I would like to talk about here is what I do to actively manage my mental health and improve it whenever possible. I cannot guarantee that it will work for everyone, but unless you are aware of how you are feeling (physically and mentally), you run the risk of being vulnerable to sad and tough times.

I discovered three key strategies that, if learned, can significantly help during sometimes dark and difficult times of your life:

Hypnotherapy – this dramatically helped me when I needed it most and I cannot thank my therapist, Andrew Workman enough. Far from all the horror stories and dramatic TV images of people being made to walk like chickens (which could not be further from the truth), I found the whole process very calming, relaxing and it helped my subconscious to process some of the problems that my mind was wrestling with. I think if I were to encounter a crisis again in the future, this would be my first port of call… It quickly makes you feel more happy and able to deal with things objectively. Please rest assured that this therapy is safe and ever so beneficial providing you use a reputable therapist. It did not change my beliefs or views on anything, merely put me into a relaxed, almost daydreaming state where the words of the therapist simply washed over me. The only risk is that you may drift off into sleep (which I did numerous times!), but I am assured that your consciousness is still active and it still works.

Meditation/Sleep music – someone recommended this to me and I must confess I did not think that I would be able to concentrate and would get bored. Do not get me wrong, it is not easy, but after a couple of times you learn to concentrate on your breathing. I used a well-known app called Calm, which provides a whole series of meditations to suit whatever you are wishing to address, i.e. anxiety, happiness, panic attacks, low mood. Providing you are committed to meditating regularly, you will notice small improvements and be more in control of how you feel. Also, like lots of people I guess, I have struggled to sleep well and encountered many nights where my mind would not switch off… like having an excitable child in your head, preventing you from resting. Listening to a calming voice telling a story is effective and it is surprising how much you recall (or not!) the following day.

Physical exercise – this is something I have begun to really love because of the mental, as well as physical, gains and would not want to live without. It does not always matter what you do, more the fact that you do something every day. I like running (not as far as I used to) as I find it to be a powerful way of dealing with my stresses and emotions. Whilst running is my anchor, I do other things to prevent getting bored. Some examples would be High

Intensity Interval Training (or HIIT), cycling, weights and long dog walks, essentially anything that gets you off the sofa!

Running however, helps me to completely switch off – which might sound like an odd thing to say. But I try to focus on the world around me: the trees, the animals, the noises, the sounds, the smells and perhaps goals ahead of me that I am aiming for. This approach distracts me temporarily and allows me to ignore and 'switch off' negative sensations in my body and keep going further. It is not an exact science, sometimes I cannot achieve it and struggle the whole time, but it is a technique you can practice that allows you to connect with your surroundings and tune in.

It would be hypocritical of me to say that I religiously stick to these strategies, I do not always. However, I neglect **all** of them at my peril and soon realise that either my mood has dropped, I'm more irritable or pick up on certain physical changes (such as heart rate increase, lack of concentration, procrastination and so on). By recognising these signs and being self-aware of what is going on, it helps you know how to react and what you really need. I sometimes describe it as a feeling similar to leaning out of a car window on the motorway (not advisable I should point out), however, you get this sense of everything rushing past you and almost a sensation of being breathless. It is when I feel like this that I know I need to apply the metaphorical brakes and simplify what is going on in my head. I see it as living in the present, anchoring in the moment, taking time to ground your thoughts.

For example: back in the Spring, I was walking my dog one sunny morning when I noticed a slow worm sunbathing on the footpath ahead of me. "What a pleasant and unusual surprise." I thought! I took the time and opportunity to carefully scoop him up (to avoid him being eaten by my dog or trodden on), examine this beautiful specimen and then place him safely in the hedgerow. Not only did I feel a sense of gratitude for being lucky enough to see this gorgeous creature, but also that I might have prolonged his life by moving him out of harm's way.

So, in summary, I have discovered that physical strength is nothing without the addition of mental strength. Life will put challenges ahead of you, it will test your character and resolve… how you react to that is what is important. I have learned the following:

Be kind to yourself, even if those around you are not – do not judge yourself too harshly, you are probably doing your best.

Take time regularly to check in on how you are feeling and what you need.

Acknowledge what is going on in that moment, name it and accept it.

Recognise what you need to help you address how you feel – are you too fixed on the past or worried about the future?

Be selfish when addressing your needs – do not prioritise others over yourself. How can you help others if you cannot even help yourself!

Give yourself credit for looking after you – it is not always easy, but it is important to.

Thank you for taking the time to read this chapter. I am by no means an expert in this subject, but sincerely hope that sharing my experiences with you might provide practical help. Like most people, I have an inquisitive mind, I like to learn and become a better person. We all deserve to experience happiness and take the time to enjoy it. Have fun.

DAVID JOHNSON

For almost 20 years I have been on a journey of learning through synchronicity, intuition and intention which has led me from difficulty and depression into a world of joy, manifestation and endless possibilities.

Based in the southwest of England, I live and work with my partner Bea as part of the duo 'Bards of Avalon'. When we were both 50, we released our first album and have been working full-time as sound therapists since 2010. Like wandering minstrels, we also love to guide others around sacred sites with storytelling and live musical accompaniment. I have a passion for taking photographs, some of which feature in our stories.

https://www.bardsofavalon.com

Second Sight

Looking back at the story I am about to describe, it seems as if there was a hidden hand supporting my every move as I went through the biggest changes of my life. After 10 years with my wife Sonia, it became clear that our marriage was no longer working and we decided that it was time to move on. I went to my father, who was living alone a few miles away, in late November 2001 and told him that the marriage was over and that I would like to stay with him for a short period of time to gather my thoughts and decide how I could move forward with my life.

He was shocked by the news and said I was welcome to stay with him for as long as I needed. I made the move a few days later, taking a few possessions with me. My office offered me counselling sessions and the first session was a few weeks later. I didn't want this to be known in the office, so I drove to a nearby railway station car park where I met the counsellor in his car like some kind of secret agent meeting. As I talked about the situation I was in, I found it to be extremely depressing and, due to the timing of Christmas and holidays, my counsellor would not be available until the latter part of January when my next appointment was agreed with him.

I went to my doctor and explained I was not really sleeping and described the stress I felt I was under and so he offered me Diazepam tablets for the anxiety and also to help sleeping.

Shortly before it became apparent that we were likely to split up, I received an offer for a free trial of a set of audio cassettes by an American self-development teacher called Wayne Dyer entitled, 'The secrets to manifest your destiny.' I decided to take the offer. So, when I received them a few days later I was intently focused, with the hope of lifting the terrible depression I was feeling.

To give me something else to focus on I was invited to go skiing in February 2002. I agreed to go, but as I'd never skied in my life, I realised I needed some lessons at the local ski slope in Gloucester. I had two lessons before I flew out. The first lesson I managed to get by, but had no real confidence in what I was doing.

My father used to watch the QVC television shopping channel which had the famous hypnotist Paul McKenna talking about his new set of cassettes called, 'Positivity: program your mind to get what you want.' I decided to order the set of tapes and played the recordings whenever I could. As I arrived early for my second ski lesson, I sat in the car park and played one of the recordings.

When I walked into the dressing room of the ski slopes, I felt like a different person and challenged my instructor to let me go down the main slope, 255m, which was not allowed for anyone who had only ever had one lesson. He happened to be the head instructor and had damaged his ankle, so was only able to stay with the beginners. He asked me to ski down the 40m slope moving from side to side with parallel turns and come back up the other side, stopping with my skis touching the line in front of him. I did exactly as he asked and stopped with the tip of my skis perfectly at the line. Once again, I asked to go from the main slope. He said, "No, this is not possible, why don't you do it again?" I shrugged my shoulders, went back around to the starting point and did it exactly the same again, stopping precisely on the line in front of him. He said to me, "There's no time for you to go to the top, but I would like to work with you next week." and I replied, "I'm sorry but that's when my skiing holiday starts."

On arrival at the airport I was browsing the bookshop and found 'Teach Yourself Reiki' by Sandy Leir Shuffrey. I bought the book, read it during the week and noticed she lived near Stroud, which is only 40 minutes away from where I lived. I decided on my return from holiday to ring her and started my training as a Reiki Healer 2 weeks later.

On the day I received Paul McKenna's tapes, I decided to stop taking the Diazepam tablets and never went back to them again.

My father had suffered with eye problems for a long time and had suffered a detached retina around 1986 when three attempts were made to reattach it by the hospital but to no avail. He was registered partially sighted. By the time I moved in with him he had developed cataracts, which had become so bad that the only way he could see the carpet to clean it was on his hands and knees. He told me that because he was blind in one eye and he was very short sighted, there was a high chance that he would be totally blind if the cataract operation failed. I was so moved by the situation that I decided to find some alternative means to reattach the retina of his eye, leading me into lots of alternative therapies.

Having completely turned around my feelings about life from listening to the Wayne Dyer and Paul McKenna tapes, I decided to search for a way to help my father to see properly again. This decision gave me focus and a very strong will to find that cure and over the coming months I trained with Michael Bradford, an Intuitive Energy Healer. I worked on my own growth as a person and he helped me to trust and believe that anything was possible. Another hands-on physical healing modality came via the Aetherius Society, after which I bought the book 'Magic of Healing' by Richard Lawrence. I did evening classes on palmistry, crystals, astrology, dowsing and NFSH spiritual healing. Over the next few years I did various courses with Rick Weinman of Vortex Healing and with Tom Kenyon and Chloe Goodchild, who both work with sound.

After each training I would go back and try many of these different therapies on my father who would note physical improvements in his body, but I could not find anything that would reattach the retina of his eye.

By June I was finalising the split with my ex-wife, after we had agreed what we wanted and explained it to a solicitor who drew up the papers. On 21st of June I went to a fundraiser run by Gloria Campanelli. I met a lady called Polly who seemed very nice and so I asked her out. She told me that she had just met her perfect partner. In reply I asked her how she did that. She said there was a guide that she followed, which then led her to meet her perfect partner. I asked her if she would post me a copy, which she kindly did and although I didn't read it, I had a very clear intention that I would meet my perfect partner when the time was right. On that very night, after my declaration that I wanted to meet my perfect partner, I won a raffle and the prize was a gong bath with a lady called Sashiva. I contacted her and booked my gong bath session for August 2002 and, from that, an amazing synchronistic chain of events led me to my perfect partner, Bea Martin.

I had booked a training course run by Jhadten Jewall which started in May 2003, based in Winchester, for a long weekend working with sound healing. It started with a visit to Stonehenge after it was closed to the public and I offered to give anyone a lift if they needed it as there was no public transport to Stonehenge in the evening. I was asked by the event organiser if I could give a lift to Bea and our life journey together began. We had many long telephone conversations over the following months and Bea made the decision to move from her home in Leeds to live with me in Bristol. The synchronicities were amazing, as it turned out she could carry on working for the same company that had an office only a few minutes from my own. As we made plans to look for a flat, my father asked if we would try all living together in his home and see how it went. So, a date was agreed for her move to Bristol on Friday, 1st August 2003.

As all the paperwork with the solicitor had been sorted out 1 year earlier, Sonia wanted to sort out the divorce to which I agreed and the Decree Absolute documents arrived on Wednesday 30th July - 2 days earlier.

We were recommended by a friend to go and see an amazing healer called Ray Brown in Glastonbury in August 2004. He went on stage with his wife and did some astounding demonstrations of healing. I asked him if I could record the session so that I could play it to my father later at home, to which he agreed. After the demonstration I asked Ray if he could reattach a man's retina and he replied yes but the glue is very thin and may not hold.

I went home and played the recording to my father who could not believe what he was listening to. I then told him that Ray felt it was possible to reattach his retina and he said he had nothing to lose, so I made the appointment.

Unfortunately, Ray did not run any clinics in the southwest of England, which meant travelling around 100 miles each way. There was a long waiting list so we did not get to see him until November. Dad asked the people waiting for their turn if they felt Ray could help and they all said yes, also pointing out the files of testimonials where client's health had massively improved after the sessions. My brother Paul and I ended up taking Dad a total of five times to see Ray. After the fifth session in May 2005, he realised the retina was reattached and he could see through both eyes.

Dad's optician was totally stunned when he realised that Dad could see out of the eye in which he'd been blind for almost 20 years and wrote a letter to the eye hospital asking them to check him for having cataract operations. On 14th June he had the first operation. I then went on a journey to Peru and was at a place known as The Eye of the Puma in Sacsayhuaman at the time Dad had his second operation. I received a message that the operation was successful and that he could see again.

I looked up the symbolism of the Puma and I read that Puma reminds us to employ patience and strategy to hunt down what we want. After 3 years my father could see again.

Synchronicity seems to run through all the parts of this story, starting from Wayne Dyer and Paul McKenna's tapes. Learning about Polly's guide, within minutes winning the gong bath which lead me straight to Bea my perfect partner.

I started with my self-esteem on the floor. I had no confidence, or comprehension of what could be possible. Yet, by being open to trying new experiences and following synchronicities, all aspects of my life have been transformed. Like my father, I'm seeing the world through new eyes.

DEV RAMNARINE

Dev Ramnarine is a Trinidad-born keynote speaker, accountant, musician, and author living in the USA. He is passionate about leadership and performance and will soon publish his book on 'Quantum Leadership™' based on his model 'The Wheel of Workability™'. He is committed to empowering, inspiring, and leaving himself and others with the clarity to win the games they are playing in life. His mission is to create a world that works for everyone, everywhere.

To learn more about Dev, follow him here:

https://www.devramnarine.com/

https://www.linkedin.com/in/devramnarine/

https://twitter.com/DevRamnarine

https://www.instagram.com/dev.ramnarine/

https://medium.com/@devramnarine

Taking Back the Wheel of My Life:
How I Overcame Shame and Being a Victim of Rape

Warning: This chapter contains references to Sexual Abuse

I am walking along the sandy shores of the beautiful Toco Beach, located in Trinidad. The sun is setting as I look out into the fiery, orange evening sky. "What a breathtaking view," I say aloud to myself. The sound of the gently crashing waves and chirping seagulls create in my heart a sense of tranquility and serene calm. The smell of the briny ocean wind overtakes my sense of smell. Staring into the horizon and marveling at the awesomeness of Mother Nature, I close my eyes and enjoy this beautiful place when suddenly, I feel panic and pain. I am teleported back to the horror of my reality.

I was being raped.

I screamed, "Oh my God, STOP! Please!" My head banged into the headboard, delivering more pain. I was paralyzed with fear. I was certain I was going to die. I wanted to survive this and tried desperately to take my mind back to Toco Beach. It did not work. I was in too much pain.

***

Three months earlier, I had been in a car accident. My Toyota Corolla was totaled, folded up like an accordion. I was lucky to walk away alive. The wreck injured my spine and required me to wear a brace. I had whiplash and it would take months before I was recovered.

It was an exceptionally low point in my life. An accountant, I was no longer able to serve my clients and therefore was not generating money. I had savings to pay my basic expenses, but little else. I was a closeted gay man and didn't have anyone in my life to love me or even to share my true identity with. A bright moment occurred when I met a handsome young man who was also a professional. We exchanged numbers and started chatting on the phone. He confessed he was gay; I did the same. It was so good to finally talk to someone who understood and was willing to listen, especially given my hardships.

After a few weeks of speaking by phone, he suggested we meet up. I was happy and excited to meet him in person again. Despite still wearing a neck brace and being in a lot of pain when sitting and walking, I was determined to go.

We agreed to meet at his apartment, a safe space where we could speak openly without fear of judgement from passersby.

Walking into his apartment, I was unpleasantly surprised. He was a good-looking and successful professional, someone who had everything together, yet his apartment was in complete disarray. The apartment was littered with dirty dishes, mildewed clothes and even a dead Christmas tree from months ago. I felt uncomfortable but was trying to be understanding. I found a couch in a corner free of mess and sat down, trying to ignore the pain in my spine. He joined me there.

After a moment of pleasantries his mood turned dark. He looked me square in the eyes and told me that he wanted sex. I looked at him, terrified. He grabbed me by the neck brace and pulled me to his bedroom. I was paralyzed with confusion; he threw me on the bed. I felt my head knock against the headboard. I still recall the musty smell of dirty sheets.

Despite the pain and terror, I could not make an audible scream or cry. I watched myself from above, like in a movie, as he pulled down my pants and proceeded to abuse me. As the searing pain tore through my body, I tried feebly to kick and scream, but I was no match. He grabbed me by the neck—the place he knew was injured—and pushed my face down into the pillow. Disgusted, I realized my struggle was erotic to him. I wanted to disappear. I wanted to be at the ocean. Anywhere but there. My consciousness faded to the safety of Toco Beach, but the pain brought me back to that musty bedroom.

As quickly as it started, it ended. "You can go now," he said, as he casually left the bed to read a newspaper. He clearly knew that he had the power and felt no culpability about what he had done to me.

Though the pain in my body was unbearable, the pain in my heart was worse. I had never known such embarrassment and shame. I stumbled home, bleeding and hurting and sobbing uncontrollably. I stayed in the shower for hours in a stupor, trying feebly to wash the experience off my skin.

For days, I laid in bed. This was the lowest of the low. Unemployed, physically debilitated from my accident and now I was the victim of an unspeakable crime. The depression, anxiety and shame I felt then was truly unbearable.

To make matters worse, there was no one in Trinidad who could help me. Homosexuality in Trinidad was a crime. The police would be unsupportive and likely tell me it was my fault. I was too ashamed to see a doctor, worried they would gossip to our close-knit community and bring shame upon my family. I refused to tell my mother, a deeply religious woman, what happened, however, she insisted that I seek God's wisdom and took me to see the pastor in our Evangelical church. The pastor knew I was gay. For 14 years I had been undergoing conversion therapy in my church. I was, in the church's eyes, possessed by demons. When I told the pastor I had been raped, he told me that my rape, and my car accident, was God's way of punishing me for being a homosexual. There was no offer of support, no suggestion to see a therapist. My mental health meant nothing, only my sins.

The months following that I had no rest and no peace of mind. It was a profoundly lonely time. I had been emotionally abandoned by my family, my culture and my church. No one cared about victims of male rape, especially homosexual ones.

Had I stayed in Trinidad, it is questionable whether bouncing back would even have been possible for me. But, by the grace of God, approximately 16 months after my rape I immigrated to the United States as an asylum seeker. While the conditions of my departure where themselves unpleasant, I was relieved to be out of my native country and in a more supportive place.

Leaving Trinidad and the unsupportive community and culture was the beginning, but by no means was it enough. Once I moved to the United States and the first few months passed by, I started realizing that the trauma, fear, guilt and shame for 'letting the rape occur' were mental baggage I was still carrying around. I literally believed I was responsible. I felt like a victim trapped in the prison of my mind and I did not know how to get out.

I realized at that point I needed help. I did not know my way out of this mental prison. The scary part for me is that I did not even know how or when I got into that prison. I only knew I had to get out.

Admitting that I didn't know what to do or where to go was humbling and eye opening. In Trinidad, having a therapist or even admitting that you have mental health issues is highly frowned upon. Being in the United States and having a supportive community was a profoundly different experience to back home. Through some friends, I found my way to the LGBT Community Center in Manhattan's West Village. For the first time, I was embraced as a gay man and as a rape survivor and my journey towards healing began.

It is the support of this environment that gave me the safety and context I needed to heal. For the first few therapy sessions, I simply cried. I couldn't talk about it. But over time, I was able to articulate the events of that day without becoming emotionally unstable. I was able to become objective about the abuse and my role in it and put the trauma of the lived experience behind me.

I also began to change my relationship to dealing with my experience of being a victim. Not just of the rape, but also being a victim of circumstance, of my home country, of the ineffective laws, of a culture and society where I could not have the conversations necessary to heal.

The unfairness and injustice weighed heavily on my mind. Some days I was sad and, on some days, silently angry. After speaking with my therapist about the events of that day objectively, it became clear there would be no justice. I was no longer in Trinidad. Even if I were, there's no mechanism or law in place in Trinidad that would get me justice. The laws were stacked against me. I had no evidence to prosecute my predator. This trauma happened and there was no external resolution to be obtained. I could not take back the events of that day and I could not make the injustice disappear. Being angry about it would not make a difference in terms of outcomes. I chose to accept that there was not going to be any justice, this day or any other. In my moment of acceptance, I found my power.

By accepting reality on its terms, no matter how unpleasant or unfair, I took back the wheel of my life. I stopped being a victim and became the author of my life and my emotions. I chose to let go of resentment, anger and shame; I chose to live from a place of generosity, kindness, understanding and power. I chose to be a force for inspiration, empowerment and clarity, for myself and those around me.

Since coming to America, I've had nothing but good things happen. I've grown as an accountant, I've been happily married for over 6 years and I'm working to support others in my profession to reach new heights in their careers.

I've bounced back from the events of that terrible day and, in sharing this story, I hope that I inspire other victims of rape, particularly men, to do the same.

LEE BIGNELL

Lee is the founder of Mobius Works Ltd, one of the South West's leading integrated services companies. A self-made entrepreneur, Lee built his career having worked his way up from an apprentice electrician, building and selling several businesses and eventually founding Mobius Works in 2017 with his wife Anita. The company now employs over 50 people and is responsible for some of the South West's most forward-thinking building projects including the Wapping Wharf development in Bristol. Lee lives in Saltford with his wife and two children and in his free time is an avid Bristol City Football and Bristol Bears Rugby fan, as well as relaxing over a cider or five!

http://www.mobiusworks.co.uk/

https://www.facebook.com/mobiusworksltd

https://www.twitter.com/mobiusworksltd

https://www.instagram.com/mobiusworksltd

Perseverance, Mind!

When I was first approached to talk about my 'Bounce Back' experience I've got to admit, I didn't know where to start. Like many men, the thought of talking about my feelings, especially when it comes to my struggles, is something I just don't tend to do day- to- day. As a business owner, a family man and someone who's always pushed myself (probably sometimes too hard), the thought of sharing the ups and downs of my career didn't sit easy.

But the more I thought about it, the more I began to see it as a positive. If my experiences can help someone else through a rough patch, be it in business or in life, then it's more than worth talking about.

Growing up in Hengrove, South Bristol, I had a relatively textbook early life. I threw myself into every sports team going, left school with five GCSEs and, like most teenage boys, didn't really have a clue where that was going to take me next. However, I knew I was willing to work hard to try and find my place in the world. After writing to over 70 companies applying for various roles, I eventually secured an apprenticeship at an electrical company. Little did I know that this tenacious attitude would be the one thing to see me through the rollercoaster ride of my career over the next 20 years…

After meeting my future wife (and future business partner!) Anita, she introduced me to her uncle and auntie, who it turns out would have a huge impact on my career. They were running a forward-thinking technology company and stood out as natural leaders and entrepreneurial to me. I couldn't turn down the opportunity to work with them, especially as they were people for whom I had such an instant admiration, so I joined the team as an engineer and progressed to senior engineer.

Whilst my friends were out partying, I found myself knuckling down - learning everything I could from the people around me and earning enough money to buy and renovate our first home. Those Sunday morning trips to B&Q, whilst my friends were just rolling in from a night out, certainly paid off when I was able to take Anita to New York - something we'd only dreamed about before.

At this point in my life everything was on the up - we had our dream home and business was booming, especially after two close friends, who were brothers, invited me to join their newly established electrical company as part of the leadership team. Sadly, this didn't last long before they fell out with the investors they had brought in to progress the business. A further company was formed and I was appointed director with the two brothers.

This was to become my first experience of dealing with business and mental health challenges - a family feud between the other two partners became so disruptive it made daily work life impossible. From a mental health perspective, the stress and pressure of being caught in the middle of a family dispute was difficult enough to say the least, but when it was directly impacting the business which I'd worked so hard on it really began to take its toll. Sick of feeling like a mediator, I decided enough was enough, and with my mental wellbeing in mind I made the difficult decision to step away and buy out my shares for just £11,000. Finding myself on my own for the first time was an eye opener - terrifying, yet also a bit liberating. Through this time, I first began to realise the positive impact removing yourself from a difficult situation could have on your mental wellbeing and, now that I was out there on my own, I knew I had to be resourceful. I've always known I'm a people person so I figured the best way of building myself back up was to pick up the phone.

After phoning round a few old contacts, I struck gold when a previous client I'd always gotten on well with offered me some spare office space and the use of one of their company vans; I couldn't believe my luck. We'd always had a great working relationship and this fast led to discussions in the office about how we could work smarter together. We pooled a small amount of capital and set up my second business - I was just 26 years old.

Throughout this time, I found that I thrived when left to my own devices. Where previously there had been a lot of opinions and politics to contend with, this new business relationship saw me making my own decisions about how best to drive the business forward and as a result, things grew. Everything I did at the time was self- taught and, having seen the pitfalls of my previous business, I knew now that I was solely responsible for the success of the business: good or bad. The same went for my mental wellbeing, as I began to see the importance of looking after that as well as my business success. That knowledge is something that's stuck with me to this day. Taking responsibility for not only your successes but also your mistakes (no matter how senior you may be), will always be welcomed with respect from your team and clients. There's nothing wrong with holding your hands up every now and again.

So once again, things were looking good. Until 2008. The recession had an unfathomable impact on the entire construction industry and after several successful years, the company and I found ourselves suffering a bad debt of a couple of hundred thousand pounds. A contract we'd been successfully working on went bust quite literally overnight. It was a huge blow. Whilst my gut instinct was to throw myself back into the business and try to pick up the pieces, I knew I had to step back, take stock and evaluate - another tactic I've carried through with me until to this day. Not only to consider my options, but to give myself a much needed opportunity to re-centre and to look after myself. After taking some time to process the gravity of what had happened, I decided to draw on my learnings from when I last found myself in a difficult situation and took the personal approach. Thankfully, it paid off.

Working on my positive working relationships with our suppliers, I managed to completely re-negotiate our credit terms, pulling the company back from the edge and saving the jobs of everyone who was working there. It was without a doubt one of the toughest points in my career, but it taught me that whatever roadblocks life throws at you, there's always a way around. After all, an expression that has always resonated with me is, 'a smooth sea never made a skilled sailor' and there have been many moments in my life where this has rung true. I know that the stressful times will help me to learn and grow and become better at navigating life's challenges, both in business and when it comes to my mental health. It's something I have to remind myself of regularly.

After the recession I stayed with the company for almost another decade. Over that time, I built on what I'd learnt in my previous experiences, building relationships with as many people as I could, trying to think outside the box when it came to new sectors, new clients and ways in which we could diversify - as well as learning a great deal about growing, managing and nurturing a team. In 2017, taking all these learnings, I knew it was time for a change. Leaving on good terms, I set up Mobius Works Ltd in partnership with my wife Anita and our latest chapter began.

Upon leaving, I found myself under a legal contract which limited the industries in which I could work; another hurdle I hadn't necessarily expected, which once again put me in a position where I had to think hard about diversification. If I couldn't call on the contacts I'd once relied on, then where was the need for the services we could offer? Again, I found that stepping back, reflecting and considering my options were my secret weapons.

We began to look at new industries to work with, approaching owners in Bristol's growing hospitality industry, incorporating new services and growing a small team of like-minded individuals who I felt shared our values. Now, three years later, Mobius is a 50-strong team of amazing people, turning over £7 million and delivering some of the most exciting and innovative projects in Bristol and beyond. To say I'm proud of everything we do would be an understatement.

When I first started thinking about what I wanted to convey in this book I wasn't sure exactly what learnings I could bring to the table, but as I've said already, sitting back, reflecting and thinking about things has really made me realise just how far I've come and just how much I've learnt. The ability to step back and also take time for yourself to look after your mental health and wellbeing is also just as important. The ability to find my own drive and push myself, no matter how tough things seem, has seen me through some of my hardest times and being able to accept your losses along with your wins without taking it personally puts you in good stead to be a strong leader.

When it comes to growing a team, giving people autonomy and allowing them to drive not only their own careers, but your business as well, is an essential part of making them feel valued and trusted as well as being a key part in keeping yourself sane. I firmly believe that if I was to get hit by a bus tomorrow my business would be able to run without me, as I've built a team around me who not only believe in what we do, but who know they are trusted to make important decisions without me.

Most importantly, I've learnt that whatever happens in business, or in life for that matter, there's always a way to make things work in your favour if you're willing to persevere. As Richard Branson said, "Business opportunities are like buses, there's always another one coming." Smart man that Branson, mind!

LUKE WESTWOOD

Luke is a digital learning professional, working for a professional services firm in London.

After suffering for 10 years, living with chronic pain and experiencing multiple episodes of depression, Luke was getting close to breaking point at the young age of 28.

Between coping with the stigma of a hidden disability, the stares when he was brave enough to use a walking stick in his 20s and the pressures holding down a job; Luke felt trapped.

This is where Luke decided something needed to change; he sought professional help that focused on using therapy. A dirty word in Britain.

Luke is now living independently and can manage the pain. Outside of his career, he shares his story of mental and physical illness and is a campaigner for ending the stigma of therapy.

https://www.linkedin.com/in/lukewestwood/

Therapy Saved My Life

Have you ever been in so much pain, all you can do is cry?

You just want to scream?

You want to amputate the part of your body which is hurting?

You feel like a burden to your family and the few friends you have?

You want to take your own life?

This was my life for 11 years. After years of seeking advice from doctors and consultants, all of whom had mixed answers or no answers at all, I eventually gave up looking for answers. I was ready to end it all.

Before I climb down the rope into the pit of despair, I want to let you know that at the age of 31, I am now happy. I have recently moved into my own flat, which I thought would never happen. My family always thought I would need 24/7 care. I also have a career, which I can do from home now. Again, this was always a dream. I feel more in control and relaxed than I ever have.

I am happy.

Although I cannot fit everything which has happened in my journey into this chapter, I wanted to share what is most important to me.

The beginning

I still remember when my chronic pain abruptly entered my life and became my new companion. I had recently started a weekend job at a local supermarket stacking shelves, which also involved pushing large and heavy containers full of food. I will never know if this job is what started my pain, maybe it would have come anyway, but I will always wonder.

The pain was unlike anything I had ever experienced. I could barely stand because my feet were burning with pain and my leg muscles were cramping and tight. Just a few months prior, I was at the gym, attending air cadets or enjoying life as a young man. But this was all about to stop.

I was only 18.

How could this be?

I should be at the peak of my health and fitness, shouldn't I?

How can I be hobbling along, just to walk ten minutes up the road?

Little did I know, this would become my new normal.

As the years went by, the pain ruined so many of those special moments in life. From my graduation at university and countless Christmases, to nights out ending in agony and family dinners being ruined.

But on top of this pain and suffering, I had to keep telling myself one thing: "Just deal with it. There are always people worse off than you. Stop being selfish."

I hate this saying now and I know it comes from social media influencers, who tell their audience not to complain about their situations. They make you feel guilty for complaining, even though you have a genuine reason to be upset. But it's all I kept hearing.

Visiting hospitals had also become a monthly ritual from the age of 18 to 28.

If you have ever experienced visiting the hospital over a long period of time, hoping for an answer, you know the emotions that come with each visit. Visiting hospitals became part of my life and that of my mum's. I have so much to thank her for: everything she did in that period but also my sister, brother and father.

With each visit we would start the mental roller coaster, usually in this order:

The anxiety built as we drove to the hospital.

Preparing for no answer as we parked, but secretly hoping for one.

The frustration of waiting to be seen.

Wishing the doctor would give us a straight answer and being too upset to understand what they were saying.

Returning to the car in both pain and tears.

The guilt of being a burden setting in on the return home.

The hunt for an answer seemed like it lasted forever. Trying so many ideas: from not eating certain foods, wearing certain types of shoes to cutting out alcohol or losing weight. But nothing ever seemed to work.

But always telling myself the same thing. There are always people worse off, so stop moaning.

I also had to get used to the idea of using a walking stick in my 20s and the stares which came with that. I now know this is called stigma and is something I'm passionate about today. I'm used to being stared at. I've had it my whole life, because of how I look. But this was something different.

This was having to use a walking stick to help my disability and being judged. Although people didn't say anything, their eyes said it all.

'Why is he using a walking stick? He shouldn't be using one at his age. Is he trying to scam us to get a seat on the train?' This is just a taste of what I felt people were asking themselves and how it made me feel inside. It also made me stop using a stick at times, just to avoid the guilt.

At my lowest

There were so many low moments in this period of 18 to 28, when I felt like I couldn't carry on. So many ideas on how to end it. So many reasons to take the pain away from me and those around me.

But there was one low moment which will always stay with me because it was out of character for me.

Having a job which involved commuting has always been one of the hardest parts of my chronic pain. I'm unable to stand for any period of time and navigating public transport is just as difficult. It also means that after any commute I'll be in agony, just as my workday is starting and it can last all day. It also means I would have to go through it all again on the way back and be crying my eyes out at home.

However, this is one low moment which will always stick with me. I had just arrived at work, which at the time was a military base as I worked for a company that helped with the military's training needs.

On military establishments they have places of worship. Because of my pains and other medical conditions, I have never been religious, but that morning was different. I was in my usual pain from my short commute and couldn't face walking into the office to start another day like this. I needed to talk to someone but had nowhere else to turn. I was crying my eyes out as I arrived and sat down silently, hoping someone would arrive to offer comfort.

Eventually someone did arrive. I don't remember his name, but we sat talking for ages as I let it all out. We had never met before, but he was comforting me. Simply talking to someone and getting all of my dark thoughts out of my head was making a huge difference. This is when I knew therapy could help, but the stigma of therapy was still strong.

That little voice in my head would keep saying, "There are always people worse off." for a while longer.

Taking the decision to get help

Fast-forward a few years and it had been a long time since I last visited a hospital. I had just given up and was coping as best as I could. But at 28, this was not going well. I had been through numerous episodes of depression and felt utterly trapped.

When everything became too much, I knew I had to try one last time to do something and get help, but I knew this could not be done through the NHS. It had to be therapy.

That is when I started thinking about something called The Lightning Process.

It is a type of therapy which focuses on self-talk and how we approach our challenges in life.

I knew about this because a family member had taken it before and it had done wonders for her, which is why I decided to give it a try. But it was a risk. I knew it might not help. I knew the emotions, which came with hospital visits, would all come back and it could be for nothing.

But I also knew there was a chance that it could help and be the miracle I needed, so what did I have to lose?

I had also stopped saying to myself, "There are always people worse off."

Instead, I was now saying, "Stop worrying about other people and focus on you."

Two days later I could walk

I went into the therapy using a walking stick and close to using a wheelchair for the rest of my life.

It was a challenging experience but, after 2 days, I came out without needing the stick and felt like a new person. The pain had gone and I felt like my younger self, before this all started.

I'm still using the techniques from that therapy today, when I do get days of pain and low moments. It's so powerful and every time it works it's a reminder to keep using it.

I'm now living independently, working at a huge company and able to work from home. Everything that I knew would help my life has happened and I couldn't be happier.

Instead of preventing myself from getting help because others are worse off, I now focus on myself, so I can help others who are worse off and need help.

MICHAEL HARRISON-HASTINGS

I am a co-founder and Operation Director of Mindmaps Wellbeing, a mental health training company based in the southwest of the UK. We provide guidance and support services beyond the initial training, suitable for the workplace or individuals. All services provided are delivered by registered mental health nurses. I believe it is time for us to keep talking about mental health in all settings. This is why it has become both my work and my passion.

When I'm not working, I take care of my own mental health by kayaking, walking, talking to friends and spending time with my wife and two children.

https://www.mindmapswellbeing.org.uk

Broken Marriages

Growing up I was the middle child of five, lucky to live with both parents, in what I believe to be a typical childhood for someone growing up in the 80s & early 90s. I recall one of my early college days in the mid-90s being only one of two students whose parents were actually still together from a group of 60. Only a year later I would join the others in the group, as I discovered my dad was having multiple affairs and had got his current lover pregnant.

The world I had known simply imploded. The family was torn apart. The next few weeks and months were the toughest I had known up to that point in my life. Being 17, people would often say it must be easier than if I had been a small child. The truth is I don't know, but what I am aware of is how, after 25 years of marriage, their divorce tore the family into segments. Not wanting to choose, I went out on my own to face the world.

I felt as though I had dealt with the whole situation incredibly well. Only when reflecting can I see that all I had done was run away. Moving to Torbay, I was far enough away from the daily grind but close enough for a visit should it come about. This was my first up close experience of a broken marriage. I vowed to myself that on the unlikely day I chose to marry, it would be forever. Isn't that true of every person going into a marriage?

Continuing with life, I made new friends and found a path in hospitality that I was both enjoying and seemed to be good at. Making rapid progress to hotel manager of a three-star, 52-bedroom hotel by 21. Who needed family anyway? I was doing well, right?

On a night out at my new local, having been in Torbay for a couple of years, I met someone very special. She shared all my interests and, to cap it off, not just liked football but was an Arsenal fan too. Could life get any better than this? We dated for a year in a whirlwind relationship before getting married in 2002. We bought a three-bedroom house in Torquay together to start married life.

Work was getting busier and the partying slowed down for me. I was spending increasingly more hours away from home, including nights, to keep up with the demand. One evening I thought I would surprise my wife by coming home unexpectedly, only it was I that was in for a surprise. Heading into the house, I spotted the empty wine glasses and dinner plates on the table; I assumed she had a friend over. Heading upstairs I heard noises that clearly, I should not be hearing. It was obvious at this stage there was somebody else in my bedroom with my wife.

I walked in on something I should never have experienced; my wife was in bed with another man. Naturally, I screamed, shouted, kicked him out and proceeded to breakdown in disbelief. How had this happened? How had we got here? I thought we were on a path to be together forever. With my strong belief in marriage, I tried to repair the damage. As the story unravelled, she revealed he had been her first ever boyfriend back in their schooldays and they had rekindled their relationship online before recently meeting. She said it had been a mistake and she only wanted to be with me. I believed her.

After so many promises and lies about the affair being over, saying she only wanted to be with me, it became evident she was continuing to see him on a regular basis. Eventually she stopped hiding it and said she was torn between us – like somehow this made it okay to her.

We began living life in a monthly cycle:

A week of intense arguing.

A week of silence while I was simply ignored; it was my fault – right?

A week of making up.

A week of enjoying believing this time it would be different, we were finally moving forward and could put all this behind us.

The problem was that everything in my life was beginning to suffer; from making excuses not to attend work - or if I did go in - being only half there, to dropping out of nights out with friends. In fact, I rarely left the house for about a year. Any excuse I could think of to not engage with people.

I felt worthless. I did not want to be part of anything. I felt ashamed. I felt lost. I wanted to give up on life. I was in a period of depression that remained undiagnosed, as I did not acknowledge it myself. I was also good at hiding it from others; talking about it never occurred to me.

I can't remember when I first started planning or thinking about suicide. I spent many lonely hours thinking how much easier it would be if I disappeared. I thought of many different options, even trying to cut my wrists a few times but never succeeding. I had no family for support and my marriage was in ruins. I could not bring myself to go to work, so told them I was sorry and would not be coming back. It must have been a relief for them, the way I had been over the last few months.

Having a good amount of medication for my illnesses, I sat thinking about just how easy it would be to have a few drinks and take the lot. That would solve everything. I would no longer be a burden to the world. I was ready to leave. The next time the house was empty would be my opportunity.

My wife got dolled up and went to meet her lover. This was my chance. A bottle of Jack and a batch of tablets. I took a drink and swallowed a handful with it. "That was easy," I thought, "what if it's not enough?" I felt fine. So, I drank some more, then proceeded to take every tablet I could find. I sat back and thought, "This is it. I will fall asleep and never wake up. Finally, this nightmare will end." I was feeling drowsy. I could feel myself nodding off and suddenly waking again with a jolt.

I panicked, "Oh s**t, what have I done? I do not want to die." I struggled to stay conscious; I may have dropped in and out of sleep, I cannot be sure. It all goes a bit hazy here. I cannot recall all the details, but the next thing I knew I was at Torbay Hospital being told to drink a charcoal drink.

Afterwards I was to learn I had called Tim, a friend I had met when I first moved to Torbay. He got me to hospital. Thankfully, I was rescued by a friend and the team at Torbay Hospital on that fateful night. I honestly believe I would not be here writing this today if it were not for my friend coming to rescue me.

My only regret is that when I found myself at the lowest point of my life I did not speak up and ask for help. This, despite the fact that my best friend Tim was also a registered mental health nurse.

That was a long time ago now and who knew then that Tim, who dropped by to help that night, would become my business partner today. We co-founded Mindmaps Wellbeing, a mental health training and consultancy service company. I am thankful every day that Tim was there to help me in my time of need.

I left my wife at that time and have found a life that I am genuinely happy with. I have rekindled relationships with my siblings and I was back in contact with my Mum for the last few years of her life (which I am very thankful for).

I even got married for a second time. This time I am happy to be able to say that Jo, my new wife, is the most amazing person. I feel so lucky to have had the fortune to meet her and enjoy every day together. We have been together for 14 years and married for 10, we have two beautiful daughters that I could not be prouder of: Trinity-Jade & Ieesha-Destiny. I value every day of my life.

The message I would like you, the reader, to take with you is that no matter how bad life feels, it is only temporary. Life will always move forward and the good times will come again; I'm living proof.

It is okay to not be okay, but it is not okay to not ask for help when you need it.

NICK CANN

I am 57; a stroke survivor and an ambassador and volunteer for the Stroke Association. Growing up in Newport, I worked at Barclays, and was the Chief Executive of the Institute Financial Planning for 18 years. I won the Professional Adviser Awards IFA Personality of the Year in 2007.

I have been married to Jo for 36 years and I'm fortunate to have three children; Jemma 26, Rhys 24 and Bec 22.

For my fundraising efforts I won the Life After Stroke Awards 2016 for raising £122,000 - https://youtu.be/qQhyAf0JBdI. My claim to fame is that Mark Goodier did a podcast on my story.

Having won the Adult Volunteer Award Monmouthshire in 2017, I am now a member of Wales Advisory Committee and Vice-Chairman on the Aphasia Advisory Committee.

https://www.stroke.org.uk

https://www.mystrokeguide.com

https://twitter.com/TheStrokeAssoc

Lost for Words

My name is Nick Cann and I am a stroke survivor with aphasia (difficulty with speech and language), dyspraxia and atrial fibrillation (irregular heartbeat). Here is my story.

I grew up in a beautiful house in Bassaleg, Newport. I have two younger brothers, Chris and Phil, and a younger sister, Emma. I was at Colston's boarding school, then went to Oxford Polytechnic and studied accountancy for 1 year, which I failed. I accepted a job at Barclays, which led to Flemings and then became Chief Executive of the Institute of Financial Planning for 18 years. It was amazing; I travelled the world through my job and met so many inspirational people. I attended and spoke at conferences worldwide, always networking and recruiting new members. It was the best job ever, leading a strong, focused team.

My wife Jo is beautiful. We met at a school dance and got married at 21. She went to Redmaids' school and also studied at Oxford Polytechnic. We have lived a very happy life, with our 36th anniversary coming up this year. Jo has had a very successful career working at Aviva, competes in triathlons and gained an MBA. Jo and I have three wonderful children of whom we are very proud.

My eldest daughter, Jemma, 26, is a senior vet nurse at Rowe Vets and has been happily married for 2 years.

My 24-year-old son, Rhys, completed a Masters in Economics at the University of Birmingham. He works at Cantab Asset Management. Rebecca is my youngest at 22. She has recently finished at the University of Leeds studying French and International Business. Bec has been travelling in South America.

Our lives were turned upside down 7 years ago when I was a guest speaker at Northampton University promoting financial planning to 50 students. Halfway through, I suddenly collapsed and was rushed to Northampton Hospital. I experienced a severe stroke. My wife rushed to hospital as soon as she heard and my children were mortified to see me lying in a hospital bed being told that I may never be able to speak again. We were grateful and lucky to know Robert Hicks, a consultant and friend who helped explain those devastating times and who made sure that I was getting the best treatment to aid my recovery.

I was moved from Northampton Hospital to St John Radcliffe in Oxford as a result of thrombolysis, a swelling on the brain. I was then moved to Newport Gwent, then to Chepstow where I spent the last 4 weeks of hospitalisation. I was happier there; my family were able to see me more and I was lucky to be placed in a private ward where I listened to my favourite music. Speech was very frustrating. My face was drooping, I was dribbling and I wasn't very mobile because I had right side weakness. I had occupational therapy at hospital to help with walking and to prove I was able to get up and downstairs so I could eventually come home and be with my family. Luisa (a stroke volunteer) visited me at home and put me in touch with stroke services. Although, I didn't receive any speech therapy for 6 weeks which is what I really needed as I could only say a few words at a time. We were forced to go private so I received 10 sessions in Bristol that each lasted 2 hours.

The therapy was helping; I was getting better. Then I had a second stroke attack whilst swimming at St Pierre. I was alone, but the people there were great in getting me an ambulance to the Newport Gwent Hospital. Jo and my daughter Bec came immediately and I was intubated for 6 hours. I wasn't allowed to drive for a whole year, which was a disaster, although I used a local support transport system called 'Grass Roots' until I got my licence back.

My recovery this time was faster, my legs got better and I felt more mobile. Walking in the garden, fields and gradually walking in the woods for several miles. My right hand was practically inactive, I had to learn to write with my left hand which required constant practice.

I started to notice changes from my life pre-stroke and post. My perceptions of myself became so much stronger. My relationships with others completely changed where I felt a greater sense of intimacy, compassion and a sense of belonging. My philosophy of life altered as well; developing a renewed sense of purpose and appreciation for my life. Every day I'm working to be the best I can be.

We have two black Labradors who I take for walks in the woods every day, generally 4km. This is a good opportunity to take time out from my day to think about everything. I go to the gym, swim, run, cycle and lift weights, which I have found helpful in becoming stronger on my right side. I play golf and tennis, which was a struggle at the beginning as I had to learn to play with my left hand. Practice has made this a lot better and I am proud of my improvements.

Speaking of improvements, the table below shows my scores in 2013 vs now based on the different factors that make up aphasia. The scores show just how much I improved over time with lots of practice.

Aphasia

	2013	Now
Drooling	7/10	9/10
Mobility	5/10	9/10
Reading	2/10	8/10
Writing Abilities	0/10	8/10
Speech	0/10	7/10
Listening/Comprehension	5/10	9/10
Numbers	0/10	5/10
Preposition	0/10	5/10
Technology	0/10	7/10

Social media is truly remarkable. I use Twitter (world), LinkedIn (business), Facebook (friends) and Instagram. I am both an ambassador and volunteer for several groups that meet regularly to talk about the news, updates on family and friends and practice apps designed for aphasia. Groups are held in Abergavenny, Chepstow, Newport and in Cwmbran. I am treasurer for the stroke choir called 'Strike A Chord'; singing has really helped with forming words and confidence. I live a very happy life, great friends, work colleagues and attend 41 Club.

I presented at the Chartered Institute of Securities and Investments conference in 2017 (around 150 people) with a video presentation and also sang two songs. This was the first conference I had done since my stroke and I was very proud of myself and of having the confidence to sing two songs! This conference offered more opportunities to speak elsewhere; for instance, a conference led by Money Marketing, Stroke Association Crewe, the Platform Awards, and others.

I've also been interviewed on BBC Wales radio by Wynne Evans. We talked about my stroke journey and the amount of money we have fundraised for Stroke Association: £122,000. I won fundraiser of the year at the Life after Stroke Awards in 2016.

Fundraising was good for me to get active, work, use social media, connect and network with friends and build confidence. I strived to raise as much money as we could with the help of friends and family. We wanted to have a positive influence on the stroke community.

Some of the fundraising events I did included 5k runs in Cardiff and Devauden. I have never liked running, so even participating in these events was an achievement in itself. Nick Richards (a friend) ran alongside me every step of the way. Jo and I completed a cycle ride from Cardiff to Tenby. Cycling was very challenging as a result of the weakness in my right side. It was very windy, but I am proud to say that I completed 40 out of the 108 miles.

Jo and friends cycled from London to Paris to raise money for Stroke Association, a magnificent achievement. Cath (family friend) organised an 'It's a Knockout' event. The amount of people there to support was incredible. I am pleased to say that our team won.

More than 350,000 people in the UK have aphasia; a disorder of language and communication. When I had a stroke, I didn't feel like I had support for my recovery. I was therefore determined to help others in a similar situation. Being vice-chairman of the Aphasia Advisory Committee and part of the Wales Advisory Committee has been very beneficial in influencing direction and improving the life after stroke for others.

Jo and I set up the Phoenix Project Aphasia initiative lasting 3 years. The Phoenix Project's aim was to work with stroke survivors and carers across Monmouthshire to increase confidence and independence and reduce social isolation with aphasia. The project received 58 referrals for people who were then supported and became part of a community. The outcomes of this movement were an increase in communication, peer support opportunities and permitting stroke survivors to feel more confident and less socially isolated. We believe that the project made a significant impact for stroke survivors.

The Future – I am a stroke survivor with aphasia; helpful, contagious smile and inspiring others. I'm confident, positive, motivated, strong and proud of my achievements. I am kind and feel lucky with my life even with the setback. I have promoted and helped the Stroke Association with aphasia month in June 2020 by promoting the use of digital technology to support others like me. I am proud and honored to have received a BEM (British Empire Medal) in recognition of my achievements.

NIGEL BRIERS

Nigel has a life long battle with depression and addiction. He has been on a journey of self-loathing and never accepted his true self. His story takes you through a snap shot of his life entering into recovery from his addiction.

Nigel led a life of denial in his 20s until he finally accepted his sexuality as a gay man.

Today Nigel has a life he never dreamed possible.

This is for everyone who has an interest in reading this. Addiction is addiction and your sexuality has nothing to do with it. Lust is common in all sexuality and it's the number one thing that we as addicts use to fix our feelings.

One day at a time life is healing the scars of the destruction of addiction & he hopes this brings hope to one person for it to be worthwhile - if it helps more, then fabulous!

Sit back and know that recovery is possible.

Email: nigelbriers.author@gmail.com

https://www.facebook.com/nigel.briers.311

Out of the Clouds, Into the Rainbow

This is the story of a gay man's fight for his life, in active addiction and beyond.

It was a Summer's day, I was heading down the M5 with a social worker and 'Fun City' by Marc Almond was blasting in the car. I was about to embark on a journey I never knew was possible.

Writing this today, at almost 9 years clean and sober from my addiction of alcohol and drugs, I have had to pause already - this is going to be emotional. I am 52 years old; my life is beyond my wildest dreams and I'm alive.

With my worldly belongings, all that was left from my wreckage after a serious attempt to take my life, I arrived in Weston-super-Mare. The choice of Weston-super-Mare wasn't about what was ahead of me, it was a choice between there or Bournemouth and it was all about which beach was the nicest. I kept going backwards and forwards, indecisive to the core.

I was suffering from a fear-based illness called addiction. I knew that a therapeutic community was a place that would strip me down and piece me back together again. I also knew the 12 steps programme was a thing of a fellowship that I could probably manipulate. I had no idea really and my ego was so big I didn't really care. After 6 months I would probably go back to my hometown and try to rebuild my life with what I had learnt in my career and restart all over again. If I relapsed it didn't really matter, as I could always manipulate my friends and family into holding me up. That was the rollercoaster of my life. How wrong I was...

Two years into my recovery I received a phone call one cold November evening from my Dad.

"Son, I need to tell you something and I don't want you to get too upset. I love you son. Your Dad has got Cancer and I've not got long left in this world."

My immediate reaction was, "Dad, do you want me to come home and look after you?"

"Son, whatever they are doing for you in Weston-super-Mare, stay there. It's the best you have ever been. Stay there and keep yourself in recovery."

The following months were difficult and I did visit my hometown to see my Dad. We sat in the conservatory and talked freely about his life, my life, my recovery; all with the ambience of some 50's tunes. In April my Dad passed away. With pain like no other, I got myself to his funeral, visiting the chapel of rest beforehand. I stood over his body in floods of tears, saying the serenity prayer. This was a million miles away from when I buried my mother whilst in active addiction over a decade before.

"Hi, my name is Nigel. I'm glad to be here and I'm gay."

Those were the first words that came out of my mouth in the treatment centre when I was introduced to the group. I was full of anxiety and hadn't got a clue. I was a lost little boy sitting amongst broken addicts and alcoholics. I was in such denial I believed I didn't belong there.

Two weeks into my treatment programme, I was at an appointment with a member of the team.

"Hi, my name is Roz, I'm your counsellor. Tell me about yourself."

I did and I didn't stop. Finally, I got to tell someone how it was everybody else's fault, how nobody understood me. I had been abused emotionally, physically and sexually and I didn't want to live anymore.

She said, "Nigel, you are such an angry gay man."

I nearly chewed her head off, "I'm not angry, I just need people to understand me!"

"Nigel, you are an angry gay man full of hurt, guilt and shame and from here on in I'm going to help you."

"How can you help me?" I replied.

"Do you want my help?" she said.

"I'm not sure if it's going to make the slightest bit of difference."

"Are you prepared to give it a try?"

"Oh, go on then."

I left that room feeling maybe something was going to happen in my life that could sort this hopeless gay man out once and for all. Maybe this was the place to be fixed, maybe it was a new beginning. I was so mixed up emotionally and I was overwhelmed by the fear of the past. Of old partners contacting me or even stalking me. I was a nervous wreck and I didn't know how to do me. I could do everyone else; I just couldn't get me. Who was I? What was I? What did I like to do with my spare time?

I had worked continuously from my 20's until being sacked for alcoholism in a large strategic organisation. I was a disgrace to my profession. I had studied to the max to get the grades, I flew through University with As and Bs. Nothing was going to stop me proving to my family, "Yeah, I might be gay, but I'm worth something." So, screwed up on amphetamines, I even went through a bisexual period and ended up in a relationship with a woman, trying to convince myself I was straight. It ended in disaster. She believed I was only gay because of the drugs and the vinyl I had of camp anthems. I look back and I'm horrified to think that my addiction took me to some way off places that I should never have gone to. How did I get myself into that situation? I blamed everyone from my mother to my brother, to my abuser, to my friends, to the way I dressed, to the way I decorated my flat. Everything external and nothing to do with me!

Visited by friends and family, 6 months passed and new friendships were formed. Then one day at a reunion, someone came and shared how they had been in the same profession and also taken the route of this endless path to destruction. A bond was formed and I actually opened my mouth, sharing honestly for the first time. I had a sense of relief, I was no longer alone. Who is she? I need her as a friend.

During the 2 weeks of winding down my treatment programme, I was starting to step into the wide world with no drink, drugs or Dutch courage to get me through. I had to go out into the world for the first time as Nigel, clean and sober. I walked down Lover's Walk and went along Grove Park, heading towards the Boulevard. Something stopped me in my tracks and I turned back and went to the Citizens Advice Bureau.

"Hi. I'm looking for a café where I can hang out with like-minded people."

"What do you mean?"

"Is there an LGBT café in Weston-super-Mare?"

"No! If you want anything like that you will need to go to Bristol, there's nothing like that around here!"

"I can't go to Bristol and I'll tell you why not – I've just come out of rehab and I'm scared I'm going to relapse in a big city."

"Hang on – I'll call the manageress."

The manageress said, "Hello, Nigel. We've been wanting to work with the LGBT+ community for a while, would you be interested in helping us as a volunteer?"

"I'm not sure. I'll need to talk it through with my counsellor as I'm not sure I can do it."

In my next counselling session with Roz we explored the opportunity together. "Nigel, you said you would never do anything after your career, but I think you should go for it. This is your golden ticket of recovery, take it and see where it takes you. It's the first step to you rebuilding your new life."

I started the next week as an LGBT+ volunteer with Voluntary Action North Somerset. After a probationary period of 3 months, I became an LGBT+ co-ordinator for North Somerset after a successful interview with some professionals from LGBT+ organisations and a strategic body. I was asked to set up a drop-in for the LGBT+ community to engage with once a month and the North Somerset LGBT+ forum was formed.

Sitting in the Italian Gardens on a nice August afternoon, overlooking the High Street, people watching and eye-balling the local talent, I got this urge to go to Bristol and seek out a gay bar. I wanted to have a few beers, find a man and become entwined in my old behaviour. A voice on my shoulder said, "Are you going to throw everything you have learnt and all you could have away? Find that woman you shared with and find her straight away."

I knew she was in a recovery café in the basement of Addaction, the local drug and alcohol support service. I picked myself up and walked briskly, almost running into her arms.

"Here," she said, "Read this." She handed me a 'Just For Today' book. Opening it at the day's date, I read it and started crying.

"I'm home I need to be here. Can I volunteer for you?"

"You start tomorrow." She replied, "No money, no perks, just turn up and we will do recovery together."

I was safe. I had no idea what was to follow. I didn't care, I wasn't acting out and I had a chance of survival.

My journey of addiction had started in my early teens with Stella Artois, it made me feel strong. I had many part-time jobs. I was a people pleaser: I stole bread from the bakery to take home to my mother. I always worked hard to get what I wanted and I isolated in my room. At the age of 17 I had enough of the bullying at home. I started a new life, moving into a restaurant chain host's house, where lads were around all the time and drink and drugs were commonplace. I got a job with him and kept partying hard on my days off or at any opportunity.

I got rotated to work one Christmas and New Year and thought, "No way am I doing this anymore." and got a job in the local nightclub. The party was on and there was no stopping me. I danced the next 7 years away with whatever I could get my hands on. Then, one day, a girl baked me a birthday cake; I was being shown affection. This was foreign to me, so I thought, "Let's give this a try."

In my deceitful ways, I convinced her and myself I could be something I wasn't.

After a period of denial and leaving her behind, I escaped into the world I felt more at home in. I was different and I needed to fuel my addiction with substances from wherever I could, with no regard for what was in the way. This ended up with broken hearts, as I had relationships with men that tried their best to keep me on track. I met some amazing people along the way, but they were never enough. This boy was living life to the full. Seeing married men behind their loved one's backs and with a habit of drink and drugs that was unmanageable. Every day and night just rolled into one until, in desperation, it was too much. Crawling around my house on my hands and knees, my life was over and I was torturing myself. I had no solution to the mess I was in and everyone who had tried to help had tried for so long they had given up. I turned in on myself and wanted to die. I had failed.

A usual morning in recovery started in my dry house by getting up, grabbing a coffee and cigarette. Playing worship songs, waiting for the bathroom, doing your washing if it was your washday, then cleaning the area designated to you. Off to voluntary work or college, depending on what your desire was. Leaving the house for 10am to arrive at the recovery café for 10.30am, when we would check in and read the fellowship's 'Just for Today'. That was my daily routine for the next 3 years, until my path changed and I focused on the community I had caused carnage in during active addiction.

I was serving omelettes daily to addicts and alcoholics who were all just trying to hold onto another day clean. What many don't understand is that we have to relearn the way we think, the way we react and the way we engage with the wider community. We have a lifelong illness that wants us dead. We have to fight on a daily basis. We can't do it alone. We, as addicts in recovery, need each other to tell us when we are as I call it, 'getting a bit funky' because sometimes, we don't early doors see it for ourselves.

One day a slightly overweight guy came in for lunch.

The café manager came into the kitchen and said, "There's your sponsor outside."

"I haven't got a sponsor." I replied.

"Exactly, go and ask him to sponsor you."

So I did.

"Will you sponsor me, please?"

He replied, "If you were told to go to any lengths I suggested, would you do it?"

"I think so."

"You need to leave the lads alone; lust will take you out."

"OK, I will."

"Good, I will sponsor you."

Into a fellowship I went, refusing to go to the LGBT meeting because this addict needed to learn. 12 steps later, that took almost 5 years to complete and a thorough inside job that is like nothing else I have experienced, this addict is working a daily programme of recovery.

Today, my life is beyond my wildest dreams, it's awesome. I live in accommodation overlooking Weston-super-Mare seafront with some beautiful people in my life. Almost 9 years clean and sober and I'm grateful to be alive. I'm Nigel, I'm an addict in recovery who is a gay man with integrity and if this has helped one person by reading this then I'm happy you have engaged with my piece. Life today is beautiful; I no longer have to fear myself. I have come 'out of the clouds and into the rainbow.'

OWEN MORGAN

Owen Morgan is a wellbeing advocate and podcast host. He explores what self awareness is and how we can use it to heal, transform and live a life more fully.

Owen has interviewed 100's of wellness experts, therapists and people with true stories of overcoming their wellness struggles. He has run a global wellbeing company and therapist network spanning over six countries.

With expert guests, health advocates and people with stories we dive into what it is to be human through the podcast. Join Owen and his friends every Sunday and Wednesday evening for all things health, wellness and transformative awareness.

https://instagram.com/awareness_space

https://podcasts.apple.com/gb/podcast/the-awareness-space-health-wellbeing-podcast-and-movement/id1500282568

https://www.youtube.com/channel/UCZgtTeE0afdnidu6YRm8zsw

My Trauma Transformation – One Foot Into Death

'Only when I saw into the darkness, did the light reveal itself and guide me back to transformation.'

2014 and I was being rolled down the hospital corridor, seeing the lights on the ceiling flash by like car lights at rush hour. Thinking, "Well this is it. My time is up." I had got to 32 years of age and, though I had a waterfall of various traumas and mental health challenges across my life, I had done my best. I was close to saying to my dad, "Goodbye Dad, thank you for everything." For some reason I didn't and I will never know why saying goodbye was so hard. My unusual illness of 'intussusception' brought with it the worst 6 days of my life; I lost nearly 2 stone as my body began to eat itself to survive. This was at a time where life was finally getting on track to be the best it had been, after years of depression and anxiety. Little did I know the very deep connection between my past symptoms and the life-threatening illness that nearly took my life.

'Only on my darkest day did I see what real suffering felt like and with it, a fire that could ignite a power of healing.'

2009 and I found myself in a hypnotherapy session in the hope it would help with my deep depression. I couldn't quite figure out why I was so sad, low and unmotivated all the time. Why I struggled to trust people and feel connected unconditionally to other people in my life. I came back into conscious awareness after being in a hypnotic trance to then burst into tears and feel my shaking body. Was that me? Was that my life? Who was that woman? Why was she forcing food into my mouth?

It was like a black and white movie of this 6-year-old being abused. A boy who felt lonely, desperate and scared. When I put all the pieces together, I realised that my childhood trauma was what had plagued my adult life. Creating many coping mechanisms and survival habits, it was all of this that would nearly take my life with an intestinal breakdown. As my 10th hypnotherapy session came to a close and I was to head into the world with this newfound understanding of why my mental and emotional health was so fragile, a cascade of anxiety and panic attacks ravaged my body. Another chapter of my healing began.

'Like a speed train of hailstones pumping around the blood stream, the trauma of memories battered my heart.'

"Can I ask, Owen, have you had any problems with anxiety or panic attacks in the last 10 years?" asked a very curious doctor, as I lay in the hospital bed post-surgery. I shared with him my years of blackout anxiety from ages 27 to 31 and how it got so bad that a nutritionist informed me that the adrenaline fatigue was leaving me exhausted. The doctor explained to me the effect that 'fight or flight' has on the functioning of digestion and overall bowel health. I was already aware of this science and the connection, but what took me by surprise was hearing from a medical professional who believed strongly in the mind-body connection. This was something that would later inform my work as a mental advocate.

The premise was that I had suffered with anxiety for such a long time, that slowly but surely my intestines became less and less functional, until one day they blocked completely and left me on the brink of leaving this earth. 7 days after my life-saving operation, I set myself a mission. 'From hospital bed to the Battle of Lansdown race': 6 months to get fit enough to complete a 6-mile obstacle course event. The day after I achieved my mission, on a sunny Sunday afternoon, I came up with a life-changing idea: The World Health Heroes.

'As the warmth of safety thaws the ice of trauma and the water flows into the river of transformational healing, we find our way to swim within the currents of everyday life.'

From 2015 through to 2018 I was the leader and front-man of a global company, 'World Health Heroes', that sought to give those on low-incomes access to complementary health services. We used crowdfunding projects to fund the therapy sessions and still allow the practitioners and therapists to earn a living whilst supporting those in need. This was to be my zero to hero journey. Using my brush with death as fuel to create change to all those suffering mentally and emotionally just like I had. This was to prove too big a challenge for my team and I, leading me to complete burnout and financial ruin.

Not every Hollywood near-death storyline leads to an expansive conclusion. What the Health Heroes journey did show was that no matter what happens at the end of a chapter, we have the opportunity to turn the page, grab a pen and start a new, exciting narrative with endless possibility. Deep within my core I knew there was a movement or project within me that would flourish and succeed. With an unbelievably amazing woman by my side, supporting my vision, I would settle into a project that effortlessly aligned with who I am and what I can offer the world.

'An expansive space reveals itself and holds you in present moment euphoria, as your true being expresses in the form of what may be called Flow State.'

Childhood trauma leaves an imprint trapped in our bodies and creates stories and beliefs around who we are and what we are worthy of. The processing of this trauma is key to freeing ourselves of past patterns and future fears. This 'stuckness' within us leaves the nervous system, mental functioning and interaction with the world feeling unbearable at times.

What if we could discover the co-regulating, self-regulating and community healing that could release us from suffering? How can we access the power of safety and deep awareness to lead a rich and abundant life?

Well, that was my mission in 2020: to learn and to share with the world. In November 2019 'Man Cove Wellbeing' was born. This men's mental and emotional health movement spawned from my passion for learning what it is to be human. With encouragement from my partner, my dive into my creativity and utter love for meeting people, an educational platform for men was created. A place to effortlessly learn about all things wellness came to be. The showman in me, along with an interest in others' wisdom, created a podcast that fills my heart with joy.

My trauma story and yours, brought together through conversation, can shift the landscape within the men's health sector. This was no longer just my story. It was that of all men and women who have a tale of overcoming their wellness struggles. Together, we could inspire a nation. For the 10 months the Man Cove Wellbeing movement flowed, it touched many hearts and for that I feel so blessed.

'As I stepped into the light shining down on the rough and dusty floor, I began to notice for the first time that I felt reborn to this place.'

This is no Hollywood story or poetic tale of triumph. It is a series of chapters that unfolded, which pulled and tugged me on to various paths. I walked them all and came across some very dark areas and many moments of light. I built many houses that were to fall but, in the process, I built a sustainable inner world that would hold me up as trauma came along.

My path may still not be set and nor would I want it to be. I looked the end of life in the face and to be honest, it wasn't as scary as I thought. My healing from childhood trauma is not over yet, but for every being I have met, interviewed or spent time with, I have collected pieces of wisdom that transformed the world I live in and for that I am eternally grateful.

My experiences have shaped me on a neurological, physiological and psychological level and that, for me, is the mystery of life. An uncertainty that can be seen as magical. It is time for me to deeply rest and create safe space that can move me towards a healing journey and to a wellness informed resilience. I will return to the world with a renewed vigor and presence to inspire transformation.

'Life is flowing right in front of you, here, now, in this moment. Like a caterpillar transforming into a butterfly. Know you can fly. But even if you don't fly, the caterpillar is beautiful too. Just like you. You are enough right now.'

PARIS TROY

Paris Troy was born and raised in Cyprus and came to England in 1992 to study Law before entering the media as a radio broadcaster, which he still does today. Alongside this, he is also an event host and compere for both outdoor, virtual and online events. He is also a fully trained fitness trainer, instructing both one-to-one personal training and group classes. In addition, he recently acquired a TEFL teaching qualification and now teaches English online to students all over the world.

He is 6 foot 4, dashingly good looking and a stunt double for Brad Pitt. (Lie)

His greatest skills are eating unlimited amounts of cheesy wotsits and frying a decent piece of halloumi cheese. (Truth)

https://www.facebook.com/paris.troy.56
https://www.linkedin.com/in/paris-troy-bb425177/

BOUNCE

'The greatest glory is not in never falling, but in rising every time you fall.'
- Confucius.

My Bounce moment involves the BBC Radio Devon travel news, some cabbage soup and a gunshot.

One of my earliest childhood memories is crystal clear: running around a 400-metre track on my own at school. Head back, chest out, little kiddy legs furiously pounding the dirt, hitting the home straight, lungs bursting. Then a dip, always a dip, as I break the invisible tape. It's that feeling of elation and freedom, that moment where nothing else matters in the world, that I loved so much and subsequently lost.

Sports and exercise have always been massive in my life. I was a skinny kid growing up in sunny Cyprus and I was outdoors and feral all of the time. My parents were sports coaches and I went to a school steeped in sporting traditions. I played in school teams, won stuff, kept medals and trophies. Next was a compulsory 2-year stint in the Cypriot military where I naturally stayed fit and strong and played semi-pro football.

You might wonder why I'm giving you a sporting CV. To be honest, I'm pretty bored just reading it back. It's not to brag; I was never competitive and never bothered about looking like a 'Mr. Love Island Six Packer'. For me it was simple: it was always about rekindling the pure, unfettered joy and childlike innocence in the freedom of that moment. Of me as that kid, dipping for the end line.

So, you may wonder how and why it all went wrong. That's both of us then!

Looking back, I guess it crept in during my time at Bristol University. Leaving tiny Cyprus for foreign soils for the first time had its usual challenges of settling into a new life and culture.

There were distractions, new experiences and the high work volume of a law degree to contend with. Stodgy student food replaced the Cypriot salads of my childhood. Sport took a back seat. And here's the craziest thing you'll probably read in this chapter: I never really felt the weight piling on. I can't explain why or how that makes sense, but I just didn't. I didn't really see physical changes at first, so I'd just plough through the KFC Family Megabucket, think I was untouchable and play my customary once-a-week football kick about in the park. I started needing slightly bigger tops and trousers. "It's fine, just a passing thing. I'll go easy on the pepperoni on my deep pan 16 inch tonight." There was always an excuse and cheeky procrastinations, which buzzed and built like a swarm of wasps. Classic denial.

During my University final year, things worsened. For various reasons, I knew I wasn't going to follow law. I'd realised my brain was creative, not forensic. So, I began my love affair with radio, volunteering to set up Bristol University's first student radio station. It was exhilarating but simultaneously I had overwhelming feelings of guilt and uncertainty. My parents were funding my highly expensive overseas tuition fees and here I was forsaking a potentially lucrative legal career for an unpaid volunteer role, attempting to enter the flaky world of media. I have to stress: my parents NEVER put pressure on me. I think I just did it to myself. I hid from it all by burying myself in more food.

By now I was big and heavy and I knew it. I've never known how much I weighed at my worst because I never weighed myself. Maybe I was too scared to do it. I was probably 16/17 stone and I'm only about 5'8". This may not sound much but compared to how I was, it was bad.

I resorted to one of the age-old escape mechanisms for anyone trying to find a way of shielding themselves from reality: humour. I figured if I made myself the butt of all jokes first, no one could make it worse and no one would feel awkward about the (literal) elephant in the room. You know how there's always the overweight guy in those American high school buddy movies, who gets all the laughs? That was me. And so it became my thing - part of who I was - and in some weird way, I just sort of accepted that this was going to be how it was. The new normal.

Worryingly, I was beginning to experience injuries and niggles, pulled hamstrings and calves, which of course I didn't pay the necessary attention to. So, what you need at this point is to figure it out yourself...or a shock.

SHOCK ONE

One of the stupidest things I've ever done: a cabbage soup crash diet - a big trend at the time. Crazily, you ate nothing all week apart from cabbage soup and the weight was meant to magically drop off!

It was exactly 10:59:40am on a Thursday morning that time stood still and things began to change. And when I say time stood still, I literally mean that. I know the exact time because at that moment I was on-air, broadcasting a traffic news bulletin for BBC Radio Devon. I clearly remember the following sequence:

I get to the bit where I update the latest on the Tamar Bridge and the Torpoint Ferries. I check the seconds I have left on the studio clock, but it's blurry and slow. I suddenly feel hot and clammy, the room starts spinning and, as I mumble something about, "The fridge and berries..." my head hits the desk. I come to, vow to go to the doctor (but of course, not till next week) and I laugh it off. But I'm only laughing on the outside: inside I'm starting to panic.

SHOCK TWO

A week later, I was playing football. About 5 minutes into the game, I stepped forward: not a sprint or a run, not even a jog. Just a step. I heard a loud, sharp bang - like a pistol shot - and felt like I'd been struck hard on my calf. I instantly assumed someone had kicked me from behind and I turned to see who I could have a go at, but there's no one near me. I put weight on my leg, the pain shot up my body and it felt like everything below my hips had turned into jelly.

The next 24 hours were a blur. I was carried off: hospitals, waiting rooms, doctors, more doctors, x-rays, ultrasounds and the diagnosis. I'm not exactly sure where in the official table of 'Most Serious Injuries' a ruptured Achilles' tendon sits, but it's pretty bad. The most depressing point was this: lying on the doctor's bed, being told I couldn't bear weight for a year and these crucial, stinging words: "With all this happening to you, you really could do with losing that weight."

THAT WEIGHT.

Despite knowing this for years, it was the first time anyone had directly said it to my face. I was staring into a bright doctor's light, but all I could feel was darkness. He left the room and I cried.

At my lowest point this, finally, was my Bounce moment. Everyone's story will be different. Mine is by no means the worst and in this respect I consider myself truly lucky. I hadn't been crippled for life. I'd never been bullied because of my weight. I didn't have a life-threatening illness. Many might read this and think it's no big deal and I'll be honest with you, there are times writing this that I've thought the same. But sometimes, it's not so much about what actually happens to you or how serious or not it is: it's about how it makes you feel and how it makes you, in that moment, see yourself and re-evaluate your life. And only YOU feel that because it's so intensely personal, because only you know the feelings of guilt, insecurity or fear that you've been harbouring or hiding for years.

I cried on that hospital bed not because I couldn't play football for a while or walk freely for a year. I cried because for years, I had been lazy, greedy, irresponsible, complacent, thoughtless, cavalier and cowardly. Because I'd run away from something without facing it. Because I feared that one day if I had kids I wouldn't be able to swing them round in the park without fearing a collapse. Because finally, after all the fat jokes I'd made about myself, the joke was on me. This wasn't just about fixing a tendon. It was about fixing me.

I don't want to bore you now with a long account of how and what I did to change. Not everyone reading this has, or had, weight problems so I don't want to get too preachy about it. But I will say this from my personal experience: don't try and force your life, habits and routine into a prescribed diet or weight loss programme. You'll rebel and react and it may get worse. Instead, truly understand what you are like as a person first; what your eating habits are and, I know this sounds odd, but what kind of 'eater' you are. Then accept that and find ways of dealing with it in small steps, almost constructing your own nutrition. One that is still informed and considered, but that fits your life and routine so that you have a better chance of consistently doing it.

Alongside this, I changed the way I exercised. As I've mentioned, I'd played the odd game of football but was also a gym member. Again, I applied the same thought process: find something that fits with my life and personality. Don't force myself into an exercise cul-de-sac where I resent what I'm doing and it becomes self-defeating. Really thinking about it, I realised that despite blindly handing over 30 quid a month, I actually never really enjoyed going to the gym. It was just an easy way out, an accepted solution and, psychologically, a way of ticking the fitness box. What I really enjoyed was being in a group, camaraderie and banter. I liked fun, variety and laughter. So, I joined an outdoor exercise group, the Bristol Bootcamp Company, who are now my friends and that's more 'me'. Over the years I joined more classes, trying out different things.

But the most important transformation wasn't the physical one. I don't have to state the obvious: we all know how physical health can have a direct positive impact on mental health and vice versa. Suffice to say that how I felt inside about me, those feelings I described when crying on that doctor's bed, radically changed. It may not solve everything, but I felt lighter in my mind...just don't let it get to a stage where it's more serious than not being able to play sports.

I'm almost done. Hang in there. Some final points:

Alongside working full time as a radio presenter and event host, I am now a qualified fitness instructor and personal trainer. In any job I do, I love to try and have a positive impact on people even in a small way. So, I take everything I've learnt from my own personal experiences and pass them on to the clients and classes I instruct.

One of the companies I work for is - yep - the Bristol Bootcamp Company. I still go to that same class, with that same lovely group of people.

And finally, deep down? Well sometimes when I'm in that moment exercising, jumping around in aerobics, instructing my own class, or surging towards the goal with the ball, I'm back on that school running track. No one can ever guarantee that I'll never get another injury, or that I won't pile on the weight again, or that I'll never lose my Bounce again. But in that moment that's so ephemeral yet so powerful, I'm that kid again: head back, smiling, not a care in the world, free. I hope that I'm able to help others feel like that too, because it really is the most beautiful feeling.

'A trophy carries dust. Memories last forever.'
- Mary Lou Retton, US Olympic gymnast.

RICHARD KERR

Richard is an accountant with 30 years' experience in the Financial Services sector. He is a keen walker, rugby supporter and dog lover; he also loves spending time in the kitchen cooking and subsequently enjoying the fruits of his labours with his wife, family and friends.

Richard has long harboured an ambition to become a published writer so jumped at the opportunity to contribute to this volume. Perhaps this is the start of a successful second career!

Richard recently volunteered to join the committee of the Edinburgh & Lothians Prostate Cancer Support Group, which helps men and their families adjust to and cope with living with prostate cancer and its treatment. Writing about his own experiences has helped him move forward and he hopes he can help get the message across to other men to get themselves checked!

You can find him sharing on the following social media:

https://www.linkedin.com/in/richard-kerr-fcca-84215623/

https://twitter.com/richkerr99

For more information see also - https://www.prostatescotland.org.uk/

THE BOUNCE BACK JOURNEY OF MEN'S HEALTH

Walk This Way

As I write, I have just returned from walking the 96-mile West Highland Way; one of the iconic long-distance walks in the UK. I first discussed this venture with my wife and a few friends in February 2019 and, at that time, the aim was purely to fulfil an ambition I had held for a number of years. I did not then know that, by the time I completed the walk, my life would have changed dramatically.

July 3rd 2019: nothing can ever prepare you for the moment you are told you have cancer. It's one of those things we all fear and, to be honest, the next 15 minutes were a blur as the nurse specialist ran through the various possible options. I couldn't really take it all in, but I was given plenty of reading material to take away and digest properly later. I phoned my wife as soon as I left the room. She was in London to attend an awards ceremony but, of course, she wanted to come home. So she rebooked a flight for that evening, for which I am thankful as I really didn't want to be on my own.

I was diagnosed with early stage prostate cancer. In that respect I was lucky as it was caught (and was subsequently confirmed by a bone scan) before it had spread anywhere else and thus was eminently treatable. However, to put things into context, at the same time as this happened, my father-in-law was in a hospice suffering from advanced and incurable bladder cancer. I had also just accepted a new 9-month contract, due to start in early August. So, all in all, it was a stressful time for my family and I.

It's probably worth, at this stage, briefly covering how I came to be sitting in the Western General Hospital receiving this news. My employer's flexible benefits package offered a health check and medical, which I opted to take every 3 years or so. In 2017, as I was over 50, this included a Prostate Specific Antigen (PSA) blood test. PSA is an antigen produced by the prostate and my level was raised. However, my GP advised it was not yet at a level to be overly concerned about, so we agreed we would monitor it on a 6-monthly basis. After hovering around the same level for a while, it then started to get higher, so I went for an MRI scan, followed by biopsies. Both of these were clear but I continued with the PSA monitoring to be on the safe side. The levels rose again so I was referred once more, in early 2019, for an MRI and biopsies. This time cancer cells were detected in one of the biopsy samples.

In the weeks following my diagnosis, I attended appointments with the consultant surgeon and oncologist to discuss in detail what my options were, what was involved and the potential side effects or complications. In the end, both agreed that in my situation surgery was the better option, so I was spared having to make a choice myself. I was also given contact details for the Edinburgh and Lothians Prostate Cancer Support Group – a voluntary organisation set up and run by men who have or have had prostate cancer and who have experienced the various treatments. Importantly, they run a buddy system and put me in touch with someone who had fairly recently been through the surgery and recovery. I found it extremely helpful to speak to my buddy and it helped put my mind at rest, at least with regard to the operation and post-operative recuperation.

In the meantime, I had now started my new role. Whilst I felt physically well and I am generally a very positive person – the proverbial glass half full type – I really began to struggle mentally with everything that was going on. I have dealt with team members in the past who have had a variety of mental health issues, but it was tough to admit to myself and, more importantly, others that I was finding it all too much.

In late August my father-in-law sadly passed away. Something had to give. I was trying to settle into my new job with new colleagues who were doing their best to pass on their knowledge to me and I realised I was not concentrating at all. I dreaded going into the office every morning and would walk around the block a couple of times before I could face entering the building. Although I spoke to my wife about this, it took longer before I could talk to my manager to explain my situation. However, I have to emphasise that, when I did so, not only was she very understanding but pointed me towards the company helpline, which I could call in confidence to discuss my issues. It felt like a weight off my mind to have told her. I called the helpline and again they were great at listening. I mentioned that the support group usually meets at the Maggie's Centre in Edinburgh and they suggested I also speak to a counsellor there.

Talking to people helped me realise that what I needed most at that point was time to process everything that had happened and to come to terms with what I was facing. The only way I could do that was to step back from the main source of my stress, so I went to my GP and was signed off work for a month. I think people can often be understandably reticent when it comes to admitting they are struggling to cope and many perhaps also feel it's a sign of weakness. But I can honestly say the best thing I did was open up to those around me and get it off my chest. Maybe I was lucky, but everyone was very supportive.

During the time I was off I quickly came to the conclusion that, for a period of time, I needed to focus on my health rather than my wealth so I resigned from my contract role. Around this time I also got a call, out of the blue, from the hospital to tell me a date for my surgery had come up in late November. So, things were now all coming together.

As anyone who has experienced it knows, surgery under general anaesthetic is quite a daunting prospect. However, as my wife drove me to the hospital very early that morning, I was pretty calm. The consultant came to chat with us just before they got me ready and reminded me that, for him and his team, this was just another day in theatre – very reassuring. The operation was carried out using robotic surgical equipment and I took up the offer of 'meeting' the robot before I was taken in. One of the major advantages of this is that, normally, there is a much quicker recovery time as the whole process is less invasive and, in fact, I was back home the following afternoon. Although it took me a few days to get back on my feet other than to wander about the house, I was determined to be mobile as quickly as possible.

In early January I joined the local East Lothian gym to give me a target and I was back in on the treadmill and exercise bike around 7 weeks post-surgery! Clearly, I had to take things easy to begin with and build up slowly, but it felt great to be able to exercise again.

More importantly, my first PSA results since the operation also came in around this time and showed the level was >0.1, which effectively means zero and is exactly what we hoped for.

By mid-February I had returned to my outdoor boot camp fitness classes which gave me a huge boost. Once again, everybody there was so supportive and made me feel so welcome to be back. As we all know, not long after this the country went into lockdown. I remember saying to my wife at New Year that I was so glad to see the back of 2019 and 2020 was going to be a better year! Having said that, I was determined not to let the situation get on top of me and instead to put the time to good use. I had planned on maybe looking for a new role in March, but decided I would be better off aiming to lose the half stone I had put on after my operation – in fact I have done way better than that and feel exceptionally good about myself as a result.

Which brings me back to where I started my story. I was determined to go ahead with walking the West Highland Way as it gave me a target to aim for in terms of my health and fitness. As restrictions began to be lifted in July, I was delighted that we'd be able to get out there and that accommodation, cafes and restaurants would largely be reopened along the route. I had, by this time, also decided I wanted to use the walk to give something back. The robotic surgery I benefitted from was largely possible in Edinburgh thanks to Prostate Scotland raising funds for the equipment so it was an easy decision for me to raise funds for them.

I am in a good place now. I am fit, well and feel mentally strong. I am lucky to have good friends, a loving wife and family and a beautiful yellow

Labrador who gets me up early every morning and ensures I go for daily walks! At the end of the day, for me, that's all that really matters.

Finally, a message to men. Please get yourself checked, especially if you have any concerns. Prostate cancer is the most commonly diagnosed cancer in men across the UK, but if caught early is perfectly treatable as I can vouch for.

SHEKHAR VARMA

I coach and mentor business owners and get a real kick out of seeing people succeed. I have been working with people in large and small organisations since 1996. I live in the West Country but don't restrict myself to a specific geographic area. I am married (42 years) and have three grown up children. I de-stress these days by hill walking, cooking and reading but have to tear myself away from the business sometimes because I can be a bit of a workaholic.

If you are a business owner trying to stay sane whilst pursuing a growth profit strategy, then let's start a conversation.

Email shekhar.varma@poweredbyshirlaws.com

https://www.linkedin.com/in/shekhabusinesscoachpoweredbyshirlawsgro wfundexit/

Losing It: My Journey Back from the Brink, Almost

2006 would prove to be a watershed year for me; a year in which my business and life finally caught up with a vengeance.

It began long before this, but this was the first time I realised something was wrong. I was sitting in a hotel in the centre of Moscow, having completed a day delivering training to a group of Russian sales executives; something I had had the privilege of doing all around the world. Suddenly, I felt this overwhelming sense of loneliness and sadness and I started crying. Of course, I pulled myself together and ignored what had happened. That was 2005 and it was a warning.

In 2005 I discovered that a business partner I had a joint venture with had been carefully siphoning funds out of the business. This was someone I knew - who I would count as a friend. It cut deep and left me with a sense of betrayal, anger and bewilderment. The worst part was I felt such a fool, how could this have happened? And as I ask the question, I realise that I saw this coming. Excuses that seemed plausible at the time can now be seen as ways he covered his tracks. I did have my suspicions, but I chose to ignore them because I had other things on my mind.

This was not something that was easy to share - certainly not to clients and colleagues. Who wants to work with someone who could be so stupid? My reaction was a combination of bluff (to myself) and working harder. Financially things were now very tight. To fund the joint venture, I had borrowed to match my personal investment, so the pressure was on to put this behind me and generate revenue and, for a time, this worked.

In 2006 a good friend and client unexpectedly died. I was working in Paris and the news hit me badly. Roger had been a bit of a rock for me, both as a client and a friend. To lose that support when I was still reeling from business betrayal was devastating, but I chose to keep going. I worked harder and creeping in, slowly but surely, was continuing isolation and stress.

2007 was a good year business-wise and I felt that maybe things were turning around, but I was wrong. In 2008 as clients began to cut back and the financial crash came along, my business fell off the edge of a cliff, followed by me. 2009 was one of the worst years of my life.

My superpower had been to be able to sleep anywhere, any time. Partly because I had undiagnosed sleep apnoea but also, I was just good at sleeping. Many things happened in 2009 that made me realise how ill I had become. The first was that I couldn't sleep properly anymore; I would fall asleep and then wake with a jerk in the middle of the night and be unable to fall asleep again. The second was that my stomach went to liquid. Any kind of conflict or talk of money would see me rushing to the toilet. I lost weight without trying. Thirdly, I started to feel angry all the time. A once patient, caring guy, I could now get angry at the smallest of things. All the frustration and anger that I felt was finally spilling over and, worst of all, I started to hear a voice in my head calling me to end it all.

Had I been an employee, I would hope a good manager would have signed me off sick. Indeed, my doctor was perplexed that I was working at all, but that is to misunderstand the nature of self-employment. Business was bad enough in the middle of the worst recession ever, but to stop altogether was to lose my income and the fear of it was even worse. I had to keep working. My doctor prescribed beta blockers and I can remember running a training course in Sweden not being entirely in the room - I was so calm. This was not the answer.

The biggest challenge when faced with these kinds of odds stacked against you is that your decision making is compromised. Everything feels quite rational and you think you are doing things for the best, but I now look back and realise that out of every good decision I made there were two or three that were rubbish. As things failed, life began to slip.

In the middle of 2009, my life was slipping away and not just because of recent events, which in my view were the trigger not the cause. I was suffering as a result of the constant travel, loneliness of self-employment and knowing lots of people but knowing no-one really well. Plus, things at home were not great. I was a really important person in many peoples' lives (I whispered), but I had let them all down, so what was the point of this? July 2009 I was at rock bottom.

It's now 2020 and I'm still alive, still in business and over the last 10 years I have enjoyed some fantastic times, but for a moment there I was in real trouble. How then, did I come through it?

First stop was my doctor who I think saved my life. First, because he listened. Never judging and, even though he wasn't a therapist, it was therapeutic. He prescribed anti-depressants that enabled me to sleep and took the edge off of my depression. I reckoned that if I could get through the morning, I could survive another day.

I started to talk to friends and family. I think I became the depressed businessman bore but they were - and are - so important and I am so lucky to have them. That said, there was no instant return to good mental health, but I was a functioning depressive and strangely there were benefits. My workload had drastically decreased and we had reduced our outgoings. For the first time in 20 years, I had the time to do other things.

For instance, my eldest daughter got me into being a film and TV extra. This kept me busy and engaged and, really importantly, out of the house. I got a part-time job, first cooking in a local café and then in a care home. Honestly, I hated it! I mean, I had been hobnobbing with the CEO's and Directors of global Plc.'s and now I was being told what to do by a teenager. The point was, it got me back to thinking straight and I got back to talking to real people. It was brilliant. With my family, I also took on a stand selling Indian street food at the Bristol Organic Food festival. We did this for 3 years running. Myself, my daughters, my son and my sister, with my wife helping where she could. I recommend it - every family should team build.

In 2010 the business began to rebuild, but I was determined I wouldn't return to the constant pressure of travel and delivery that had been routine before 2009. I had acquired new clients and kept them to a few, but gave them my all. I kept my time and the new activities that I had acquired.

I still have times of overwhelm and that is probably the lasting legacy of my breakdown even today. I have to be careful that I don't have too many things happening at once, although one of my mantras is, 'Life is simply too short not to try everything.' But take that with a hefty pinch of salt.

The issues that I had before my world collapsed were strangely of my own making, but understandably so. I would like to think I was too arrogant to ask for advice, but the truth is I was too scared, afraid that people would see through me and realise that I was masquerading as a business person. Imposter Syndrome is what they call it. There was some arrogance too, born from being successful at doing something that came easily. If only at my most successful I had engaged with a coach or a Financial Director whom I trusted, maybe when I proposed to send another batch of money across to my partner they would have said, "You're going to do what?!" Maybe they would have gotten me to look at how my business worked and find better ways to grow than just throwing money at it. The phrase, 'What got you here isn't necessarily what will get you there.' lingers strongly in my mind.

So here are some final thoughts:

Build a network of support people you can talk to if it goes wrong, they might just save your life.

When things are going well is exactly the time for you to seek a coach to guide you.

Get help; reaching out is not a weakness and remember decision making when you are depressed is never a good idea - at least wait until after lunch.

AFTERWORD
by Jason Conway

The world today is constantly changing and for men living in modern times, the expectations are great. The stereotypical male is strong, independent, a leader, a fighter, in control, unaffected by emotion, confident and in charge of their destiny. Since we learned to hunt and gather and form those early communities, little has changed in how we, as men, are expected to function.

As boys, we soaked up stories of men battling monsters, navigating treacherous seas, or embarking on amazing journeys of discovery. Men that did the impossible. They were heroes. What we didn't have, back then, was the permission to admit our fears and failings, to break age old stereotypes. We had no role models that guided us to understand our emotions, encourage us to ask for help and be okay with being vulnerable.

The digital age and more specifically, the age of social media, has created a pressure cooker of emotion. We are interconnected, always accessible and we have the added weight of wider social groups. Amidst the negativity and risk, is a powerful opportunity to speak up and be heard. We have the ability and freedom to tell our stories, whatever they may be, not just to a close circle of friends but potentially, anyone that sees, hears or reads our stories, anywhere in the world.

Mental health has finally been recognised as a positive topic of discussion. It really is okay to talk. Men have been given permission to open up, without the fear of guilt or blame. This is a truly wonderful thing and a powerful revelation for many and I, for one, have greatly benefited from the support of others during recent times. What I have learned, is that openness is not a weakness, it's a strength, a strength that heals invisible wounds and drives positive change.

Having strong mental health is such an important tool in life but to have it, we need to be nurtured, nourished and loved. We need to know that we matter and we need to have the emotional intelligence to let others know, when we are struggling.

Stories of people bouncing back from adversity, inspire us. They give us hope and hope is life changing. This book is filled with real life accounts of just that, the will to face challenges and adapt to change, positively. They bring us the inspiration that men can and do bounce back. I hope that this book helps others to cope and grow in troubled waters but also encourage us to share our cargo, break free from restrictive nets, steer us to dry ground and enable us to build stronger boats, for all weathers.

I used to love playing 'Wallie' as a child. Whilst it could be played with friends, I loved to play alone. This simple solitary game involved kicking a football against a wall. A game that just needed my feet, a ball and a wall and where the ball always bounced back. To use this as an analogy for life, think of the ball as you or me and think of the foot that kicks the ball, as being adversity. If we have the right tools, like a well-rounded ball, it doesn't matter what kicks us. We can bounce back from whatever walls we run into.

It's All In The Bounce

I'm told what to think and what to do,
To man-up, stand straight, stiff lipped,
Shush the voice inside that tells me to cry,
Because it seems, mine is to do or die.

I'm told to be strong and bold in life,
Be the man in charge of my direction,
Shut the door of suppressed emotions
And all those silly 'girly' notions

But since when were feelings feminine?
When, in fact, we need to think in balance.
Should I ever fall from life's bumpy wagon,
will I have the strength to face my dragon?

Am I supposed to live a stereotype?
Conditioned from birth to not flinch,
My life is always under expected pressure
But if it breaks, how will I measure?

You see, I don't want this heavy baggage,
So, I'll unbuckle, learn how to be nimble.
Whatever the struggle or the task at hand,
It's good to talk, to ask and understand.

I've realised, I'm happy with being me,
That I need love and support to thrive,
That having self-knowledge is wealth
And it's never weak to embrace mental health.

So, should I hit a wall that blocks my path,
I'll know to pause and take a deep breath,
Dust myself off and get back on track,
Yes, I will have the will to bounce right back!

ABOUT DISCOVER YOUR BOUNCE!

Discover Your Bounce has emerged as a group of companies to provide a platform for wellbeing and inspiration, to support each other and to learn from our collective experience.

Discover Your Bounce Publishing specialises in inspirational stories and business books. We provide mentoring for authors and support from inception of your idea through writing, publishing and cheerleading your book launch. If you have an idea for a book, or a part written manuscript that you want to get over the line, contact Nicky or Sharon on the links below.

Discover Your Bounce For Business provides support for employers who want to improve the staff wellbeing, engagement, culture and performance of their business. We work with CEOs, HR Managers or department heads using practical, easy to implement techniques that create instant change. As we go to print, we have worked with over 2000 employees across the country from a variety of industries and have delivered keynotes at some fantastic international conferences and events.

My Wellbeing supports individuals through individual mentoring and online courses to improve their energy and vision. If your get up and go has got up and gone, get in touch and get bouncing or choose your programme at www.discoveryourbounceacademy.com.

Sharon and Nicky are available to discuss speaking opportunities, wellbeing workshops or private mentoring:

Nicky@discoveryourbounce.com
Sharon@discoveryourbounce.com

You can also find out more on our website:

https://www.discoveryourbounce.com

JOIN US!

You are now part of our community and we would love you to join our Facebook group:

https://www.facebook.com/groups/DiscoverYourBounceCommunity.

THE BOUNCE BACK TRILOGY

The original Bounce Back Journey was published in February 2020, with no idea of the challenges that were to come. The series continues with The Bounce Back Journey of Women's Health and The Bounce Back Journey of Men's Health, published in November 2020.

COMING IN 2021

The Bounce Back Journey of Careers and The Bounce Back Journey of Parenting are coming soon – register your interest by emailing us at info@discoveryourbounce.com.

SOCIAL PASSION PROJECT

Royalties from these books fund our Social Passion Project, providing mental health awareness training and supporting other important mental health projects. Read more at:

www.discoveryourbounce.com/socialpassionproject.

REFERENCES FOR UK AND US ORGANISATIONS

Anxiety

https://www.anxietyuk.org.uk
https://adaa.org/

Child and Youth Mental Health

https://www.otrbristol.org.uk
https://www.childline.org.uk/
http://teenmentalhealth.org/

Suicide Prevention

https://www.spbristol.org
http://www.samaritans.org.uk or Call 116 123
https://www.papyrus-uk.org (People under 35)
https://www.samaritansusa.org/
https://suicidepreventionlifeline.org/
https://www.thecalmzone.net

Depression

http://www.mind.org.uk
https://www.dbsalliance.org/

Sexual Abuse

https://www.thesurvivorstrust.org/
https://www.rainn.org/

Domestic Abuse

https://www.nationaldahelpline.org.uk
https://www.thehotline.org/

Rape Helpline

https://www.rapecrisis.org.uk
https://thercc.org/get-support/https://www.rainn.org/

Prostate Cancer

https://prostatecanceruk.org/
https://www.pcf.org/
https://www.prostatescotland.org.uk/

Stroke

https://www.stroke.org.uk/
https://www.stroke.org/en

Alcoholics Anonymous

https://www.alcoholics-anonymous.org.uk/
https://www.aa.org/

Addiction

https://ukna.org/
https://www.na.org/
https://www.wearewithyou.org.uk/
https://americanaddictioncenters.org/

"The ultimate measure of a man is not where he stands in moments of comfort and convenience, but where he stands at times of challenge and controversy."

Martin Luther King Jr.

Printed in Poland
by Amazon Fulfillment
Poland Sp. z o.o., Wrocław

65079437R00066